Blabberhead Bobble-Bud & Spade

SELECTED POEMS | OF JOHN CIARDI

Blabberhead Bobble-Bud & Spade

SELECTED POEMS | OF JOHN CIARDI

Edited by Anna M. Aschkenes

Assisted by Catherine M. Nicola

Illustrated by
ROBERT J. BYRD
EDWARD S. GAZSI
LONNI SUE JOHNSON
CHARLES H. WATERHOUSE

Middlesex County Cultural and Heritage Commission

Art direction, book design and production have been
accomplished by Fran Gazze Nimeck of North Brunswick,
New Jersey. As book designer for such clients as Doubleday,
Random House and Scribner's, she has received numerous awards
for design excellence from the American Institute of Graphic Arts
Book Show; Creativity/Art Direction Show; Art Directors
Club of New Jersey; Society of Scribes, among others.

Funded in part by the:
Middlesex County Cultural and Heritage Commission
Middlesex County Board of Chosen Freeholders

This publication has been made possible by a generous grant
from the New Jersey State Council on the Arts/
Department of State.

NEW JERSEY
STATE
COUNCIL
ON THE
ARTS

Foreword

With the passing of John Ciardi, the literary community suffered a great loss. Although his mighty pen would never again be put to paper, his voice — his words — will echo forever in the minds of his readers.

Recognition for the accomplishments of John Ciardi has been worldwide: he has been acclaimed as a poet and literary critic, as a scholar and an educator. His mastery of the art of storytelling is similarly renowned, a gift we would like to share with the people of Middlesex County and New Jersey.

His perceptive observations of life, the building blocks of many of his writings, were often given humorous interpretation in the body of his works, written for children. For the youthful reader, a bond is immediately established with the author, as he jocularly unfolds a story, familiar to them. To the adult, either reading aloud to a child or reading for their own enjoyment, Ciardi's poems evoke the emotions and memories of childhood experiences.

Blabberhead, Bobble-Bud & Spade contains a sampling of works, from the more than 14 books of children's poems written by John Ciardi. Many of the pieces had been written for and about each of his three children, Myra, the oldest, John L., and Benn, the youngest. Those works which hold special meaning to the Ciardi children, now adults, and to Mrs. Judith Ciardi, have been included in this publication, and are among those which have been illustrated.

Blabberhead, Bobble-Bud & Spade has been published to share with you the whimsy and genius of this great man, so that you may delight in his writings, hear the echo of his voice, and always remember John Ciardi.

Anna M. Aschkenes, Executive Director
MIDDLESEX COUNTY CULTURAL AND HERITAGE COMMISSION

Acknowledgments

The Commission is extremely grateful to Mrs. Judith Ciardi for her invaluable assistance in publication of *Blabberhead, Bobble-Bud & Spade*. Her guidance and advice have been most welcomed.

Working with Judith Ciardi has been one of the great pleasures of this project; she is a vibrant woman with sparkling personality and wit. One of her two personal selections for the book was "The Happy Family." We can only assume the joy in the Ciardi family was chiefly due to Judith's effervescence and outlook.

The Commission is proud to make the gift of this publication, in memory of John Ciardi, to the citizenry of New Jersey.

James E. McGreevey, Chairman
MIDDLESEX COUNTY CULTURAL AND HERITAGE COMMISSION

Preface

John Ciardi was an internationally famous poet and much more. Despite the fact that he was often touring with his lectures and speaking all over the world, John was never too busy to lend a hand to his community.

Be it a visit to a classroom of eager children to whom he read his poetry, assisting the PTA's, or serving on the Metuchen Library Board, he was always there when called upon.

To the residents of Metuchen Borough, John Ciardi was more than merely a celebrity, he was part of the vitality of our town.

I am proud to have been counted as one of his many friends.

Donald J. Wernik, Freeholder
LIAISON TO THE MIDDLESEX COUNTY CULTURAL AND HERITAGE COMMISSION

EDITOR'S NOTE: Donald Wernik, a long time resident of Metuchen, was also the borough's mayor for 10 years.

Contents

John Ciardi 1916–1986

John Ciardi, who had been born of Italian immigrant parents in Boston on June 24, 1916, at the age of five, moved with his family to Medford, Massachusetts. He attended Bates College in Lewiston, Maine, later transferring to Tufts College in Medford, where he took his first degree in 1938. As a scholarship student at the University of Michigan, he received a master's degree the following year.

Ciardi had begun writing poetry while still a student, publishing his first book of poetry, *Homeward to America*, in 1940, at the age of 24. He left his position as English Instructor at the University of Kansas City, in 1942, to serve in the Air Force during World War II, and was later decorated with the Air Medal and Oak-leaf Cluster, for his service.

After the war, he was appointed to the Briggs Copeland Assistant Professorship at Harvard, where he remained until 1953. Ciardi was for many years associated with the Bread Loaf Writers Conference at Middlebury College in Vermont, lecturing during this period on a variety of subjects, and serving as its Director from 1956 to 1972. He also was Poetry Editor for the *Saturday Review*, where he established himself as a prominent and unsparing critic of modern poetry.

After leaving Harvard University in 1953, he joined the faculty of Rutgers University in New Brunswick, New Jersey, remaining until 1961. From then on, he dedicated himself to writing, to editing a "Browser's Dictionary" on etymology, and to producing a radio program for National Public Radio entitled, "A Word In Your Ear," also dedicated to etymology, one of his favorite subjects.

John Ciardi received many awards during his lifetime, including the Prix de Rome, in 1956, and the award for excellence in children's poetry from the National Council of Teachers of English, in 1982. The author of over 40 books of poetry, he is perhaps best known for his translation of Dante's *Divine Comedy*, for which he was internationally acclaimed; his volumes of children's poetry, and *How Does A Poem Mean?*, a popular, college level textbook.

Keenly aware of the attainment of literary greats — he especially admired

Dante, Shakespeare and John Donne — he insisted, in a 1950 declaration of poetic principles, that "a poem should be understandable," "poetry should be specific" and that "poetry should be read aloud," thus distancing himself from much of the (then current) academic, intellectual tradition. On the other hand, he would not tolerate the notion, prevalent during much of the following decade, that there is an overriding, egalitarian principle in art, whereby critical evaluations of artistic worth are obviated, and "all art is essentially good." This, he felt, is most decidedly not the case. These attitudes are clearly discernible in the body of his poetic work, which can be understood, and which never patronizes.

Ciardi was, in his personal as well as his professional life, a champion of mainstream, common-sense values. A family and community man, he often was requested to provide the commencement address for educational institutions in his native Middlesex County, New Jersey, Rutgers the State University and Middlesex County College, among them. He was something of a fixture in the classrooms of the local, public schools and in the Metuchen Public Library, talking to children of all ages, about poetry. Only a man as firmly grounded in the intellectual tradition as he was, and one of such impeccable, scholarly credentials could afford to be so completely beyond pretension.

Not only was Ciardi extensively involved in community affairs, he was an involved family man. It was his daughter, Myra, who publicly praised both him and his work, saying that, in the weeks that followed his death, she turned many times to his books. "I miss him very much," she said, "and I'm sure a lot of people...do. The tapestry of his life was filled with so many colors."

At the time of his death, eulogies poured in from famous writers, including his friend Isaac Asimov, who called him "fearsomely outspoken and intelligent, a master storyteller," and "a great poet." John Updike praised his translation of Dante, calling Ciardi "the most robust poet I've ever known."

John Ciardi died in Metuchen, New Jersey, on March 30, 1986.

Blabberhead Bobble-Bud & Spade

SELECTED POEMS | OF JOHN CIARDI

As I Was Picking A Bobble-Bud

As I was picking a bobble-bud
    Out in the bangle-thicket,
A Crow with a voice the color of mud
    Lit on a croquet wicket.

"Hang the mallet and pull the stakes
    And clear the lawn for wishing.
The Needles are bringing prickle-cakes,
    And all the Threads are fishing."

But I was after a bobble-bud
    There in the bangle-thicket,
And though his voice was the color of mud
    I would not buy a ticket.

"Be hanged to your mallet and stakes," I said.
    "Be hanged to your voice like mud.
I've yet to see the Needle or Thread
    That's worth a bobble-bud.

A bobble-bud will not be sewn:
    You wear it in your heart.
And once you do you're never alone,
    Though the world be miles apart.

It wants no ticket, it wants no crowing,
    It wants no prickle-cakes or fish.
And once it's in your heart and growing,
    It's all there is in the world to wish."

About Eskimos
(And Why They Wear Pants)

The Eskimo wears pants because
    He makes them out of fur.
When he gets home he sits and thaws,
    And thaws his wife, and sings with her:
        Brrrr! Brrrr! Brrrr! Brrrr!

Some Eskimos are known to wear
    Pants made of seal. Others prefer
Walrus, snow fox, polar bear.
    But all of them wear fur.

A tailor for the Eskimo
    Must sew his pants up tight,
Or else when winds begin to blow
    The frost is apt to bite.

That's why the Eskimo wears pants
    Inside the pants he wears.
He's not inclined to take a chance
    With those sharp arctic airs.

The pants he wears inside the pants
    He wears are made of fur.
And—as you may see at a glance—
    The pants he wears *outside* are, sir.

Inside and out and all his life
    He wears his pants of fur.
So does—or so I'm told—his wife
    When he comes home and sings with her
        Brrrr! Brrrr! Brrrr! Brrrr!

One oddly gentle Eskimo
    Used seals but wouldn't skin 'em.
He thought that much too cruel, so
    His seal skins had seals in 'em.

The trouble was the seals grew fat
  Which made his pants grow tight.
Seals, moreover, bark. And that
  Kept him awake—six months a night.

Worse, when he took a step one way
  His pants would wriggle somewhere else.
His neighbors often stopped to say,
  "We recommend plain pelts."

Also, of course, he had to catch
  And feed his pants a lot of fish.
One day I saw his left leg snatch
  A trout right off the dish.

And worst of all, when he lay down
  To sleep, his pants inclined
To flip and flop and slip away.
  But still he didn't mind.

Not, that is, until one night
  When he was napping on his sled.
His left leg got into a fight
  With the right—and bit the thread!

Oh, what a scene! In my mind's eye
  (Except that my mind reels!)
I see his pants go slithering by—
  An unstitched pack of seals!

His outer pants, escaped, send back
  Their far, wild call. What hero
Could tame the wild blood of the pack?
  Ours feels a breeze (well below zero).

He sees more seals go slithering free.
  By putting two and two together
He need not even look to see
  Why he so feels the weather!

See, see our hero in the throes
Of passion, but too short of clothes
To mount a hot pursuit of those
Ungrateful pants. Too well he knows
That they are gone among the floes.
Gone! Gone! All gone! And the wind blows.
He feels a coldness in his toes.
He stomps, but still the coldness grows.
Next morning passing Eskimos
Remark, "He's friz! — Or is it 'froze'?"
— Their grammar, as you might suppose,
Is shaky. But the question shows
They think about it. — Friz or froze,
They bury him among the snows,
And leave him there. And each man goes

Back home just part friz — (froze?) — because
   His pants are made of fur — skinned fur.
And each man of them sits and thaws,
   And thaws his wife, and sings with her:
      Brrrr! Brrrr! Brrrr! Brrrr!

Samuel Silvernose Slipperyside

Samuel Silvernose Slipperyside
Lived on an Iceberg high and wide.
He slept all night in his Iceberg Cave,
And he fished all day in the Silver Wave,
And he carried his catch through the Crystal Floes
Carefully balanced on his Nose,
And he sang as he hurried to and fro,
And he never caught cold at Forty Below.

And all the Seals from Nome to the Pole
Said, "There's a good one, 'pon my soul!
He catches more fish in a day
Than all the young ones in the Bay.
And there's not another in all the Floes
Has such a Silver Balancing-Nose."

In fact, the neighborhood pointed with pride
To Samuel Silvernose Slipperyside.

Samuel Silvernose Slipperyside
Heard them talk and swelled inside.
"As soon as Spring comes round," said he,
"I'm off across the Silver Sea.
Everybody says I'm good:
The place for me is Hollywood.
There I will balance Canes and Cats
Rubber Balls and Baseball Bats
Vinegar Bottles and Tall Silk Hats
Eels and Lamps and Shoes with Spats,
All on my Silvery Nose."

So Spring came round and the Whales came North
And Samuel Silvernose sailed forth.

"You'll be sorry you ever left home,"
Said Wise Old Seals from the Pole to Nome.
"You'll be sorry, 'pon my soul,"
Said Wise Old Seals from Nome to the Pole.

"You'll wish you had your Iceberg Cave
When the Sea Lion jumps from the Silver Wave."

Samuel looked across the sea
And shook his head. "I can't agree.
Icebergs are no place for me."

And so he shed his winter coat
And hitched a tow from a Whaling Boat
As far as Bristol Bay, then took
A steamer out around the Hook,
And down the coast to Aberdeen,
And then a Tug Boat painted green.

"This is more like it," Samuel cried,
"Sailing along on the ocean wide.
Towed along on a Silver Wave."
And he thought of home and his Iceberg Cave
And of what the Wise Old Seals had said.
And laughed and laughed and shook his head.

He passed a school of Silver Fish
And scooped them up in a Seaweed Dish.

He passed a school of Corkscrew Eels
(The favorite food of traveling Seals)
And he caught enough for a dozen meals.

And laughing and feeding and feeling brave
He sang all day to the Silver Wave,
Until they came to the Sea Lion's Cave,
And saw the Sea Lion on the shore,
And heard the Sea Lion roar.

"Here's where I leave you!" cried the Wave,
And hid in the rocks by the Sea Lion's Cave.

"Swim for your life!" said the Morning Tide.
"I'll swim faster!" the Sea Lion cried.

And some say Samuel replied,
But I understand from the Morning Tide
That long before he *might* have replied,
Samuel Silvernose Slipperyside
Was being worn by the Lion — inside.

And Wise Old Seals from Nome to the Pole
Said, "I knew it, 'pon my soul!"
Wise Old Seals from the Pole to Nome
Shook their heads and said, "Stay to home!"
Whenever a Seal with a Silver Nose
Balanced his catch through the Silver Floes.

And right or wrong, it's bad for a Seal
To be the Sea Lion's morning meal.

Which wouldn't have happened, except for Pride,
To Samuel Silvernose Slipperyside.

Bear With Me And You May Learn

The strangest bear I ever saw
Was back in eastern Arkansas.
  He was polka-dotted yellow and blue
  On day-glow pink with a purple shoe
On — I think — his left hind paw.

This bear I saw — that I *think* I saw —
Had three green whiskers on his jaw.
  His ears were red. His tail was white.
  As bears go, he was quite a sight,
Even in eastern Arkansas.

He swam the river to Tennessee,
Leaving a trail I couldn't see.
  It's hard to trail a swimming bear.
  When you look for his tracks, they're just not there.
Yet, where else could they be?

He swam the river and turned it green
With orange stripes, and in between
  Those stripes were some in yellow and blue,
  And one the color of chocolate goo
That was very hard to clean.

The sheriff came from Arkansas.
He caught the bear by the left hind paw —
  A rather shrewd thing for the sheriff to do.
  That, you recall, was the paw with the shoe.
So the bear just couldn't claw.

The sheriff came from Arkansas.
He caught the bear by the left hind paw.
  He put him in jail and he left him there.
  I'm not at all sure he was being fair,
But a bear like that is against the law.

He stayed in jail for a year and a day.
When they let him out, he ran away
  And hid in the woods. The woods turned red

Bear With Me And You May Learn

Edward S. Gazsi

And yellow and brown. "Oh! Oh!" he said,
"I've done it again!" And he had, I'd say.

The sheriff came to trail the bear
For changing the woods. There was no trail there.
    Or if there was, the leaves came down
    And colored it red, and yellow, and brown.
And the bear was gone—I don't know where.

The sheriff hunted according to law
Through every county in Arkansas.
    He hunted here. He hunted there.
    He never found a trace of the bear.
Not so much as the print of a paw.

The sheriff said: "I must catch that bear
Or he'll color the whole world wrong. Now where
    Could he have gone? According to law
    A bear that isn't in Arkansas
Must be somewhere else. I must look for him there."

So the sheriff hunted, according to law,
Through all the states *around* Arkansas.
    He saw six states before he was done.
    You already know Tennessee is one.
Can you name five more the sheriff saw?

He looked for seven days and a night.
—At least he did when the sun was bright.
    He saw all the states around Arkansas.
    Once you have named the states he saw,
Can you draw them for me and color them right?

P.S. He never caught the bear.
I'm glad he didn't. I don't care
    If the bear *did* get his colors wrong.
    He tried his best as he went along.
And that's good enough. What's fair is fair!

About Moose
or,
To Hairy Cows, The Hairy Bull
Is Handsomer Than Horrible

Bull moose are beastly and contrary,
Ornery, horned, humped-up, and hairy.
It seems hard to imagine how
A bull moose could attract a cow.
But every spring the mooselets come
To prove he must attract her some.
Perhaps because, though hornless, she
Is just as downright ornery
At times, and as humped-up as he.
She's just as hairy certainly.

Whatever it is that makes him seem
The answer to a girl-moose dream,
He's all the answer Mrs. Moose gets.
And every spring—here come the mooselets.

It seems just as mysterious
To ask what makes him serious
About her. But we must allow
Ladies their secrets. Anyhow,
There are the mooselets every spring.
Proving—if they prove anything—
It must be true what Noah knew
About the animals two by two.

However beastly and contrary,
Ornery, horned, humped-up, and hairy
Moose (bull or cow) may seem to be
To such non-moose as you and me,
Clearly whatever first made moose meant
To provide them some inducement
To shun mere sentimental looseness
And yearn for one another's mooseness.

Else mooselets would be far and few.
And so should I. And so would you.

The Man Who Sang The Sillies   Edward S. Gazsi

The Man Who Sang The Sillies

I met a man with a triple-chin.
Whenever he smiled, his chins would grin.
The strangest sight that ever I saw
Was a smile with three grins in its jaw.

"How do you do, do you do, do you do?"
He said to me, "Are you, you, you
Going to come my, come my, come my way?
Be quick for I haven't all day, day, day."

"I'll be happy to come, come, come," said I.
"Young man," said he, "will you tell me why
You have to say everything three times over?
It's a very bad habit, you'll discover."

"I'm sorry," I said, "I...I...I..." "Hush!
It's time for the singing. We'll have to rush.
This way! — Come along, come along, come along."
And off he ran as he sang this song:

Oh, The Sillies are the sweetest that I know:
   They have grins as big as tickles,
   They have titters up their sleeves,
   They make faces dill as pickles,
   And they spin like autumn leaves.
   They have cheeks as red as cherry,
   And they're always losing shoes,
   But they're very very very very
   Easy to amuse.
   You need only call their names
   And they start their giggle games.
   They go scramble-clatter-thump across the floor.
   They go tumble-flopping in and out the door.
   What a screech and clatter! What a roar!
But I always think when it comes time to go
That The Sillies are the sweetest that I know.

Yes, The Sillies are the sweetest that I know.
   They're a nuisance, they're a bother.

They're an everlasting noise.
Sillies act like one another.
Sillies act like girls and boys.
Sillies think it's necessary
Not to like what they are fed.
They are very very very very
Hard to put to bed.
You need only say "Bedtime..."
And they run away and climb
Up the chimney, up a moonbeam, out of sight.
Till they're caught and snuggled tight.
Then they yawn and say "Goodnight...."
And their voices are so soft away and slow,
That I have to think when it comes time to go
That The Luckies are The Happies, and The Happies are The Sillies,
And The Sillies are the sweetest that I know.

I Wish I Could Meet The Man That Knows

I wish I could meet the man that knows
Who put the fly on my daddy's nose
When my daddy was taking a nap today.
I tried to slap that fly away
So Daddy could sleep. But just as my hand
Came down to slap him, the fly jumped, AND
I hit with a bang — where do you suppose? —
SMACK ON THE END OF DADDY'S NOSE!

"Ow!" cried Daddy, and up he jumped.
He jumped so hard that he THUMP-BUMPED
His head on the wall.
                        Well, I tried to say,
"See, Daddy, I slapped the fly away."
And I should think he would have thanked me.
But what do you think he did? He SPANKED me!

"I was just trying to help!" I said.
But Daddy was looking very red.
"For trying to help, I have to thank you.
But for that smack on the nose, I'll spank you!"
And up in the air went his great big hand
As he said, "I hope you understand
It's my nose I'm spanking for, not the fly.
For the fly I thank you."
                        And that is why
I wish I could meet the man that knows
Who put the fly on my daddy's nose.
For when I find him, I want to thank him.
And as I do, I want to spank him.

Fast And Slow

Edward S. Gazsi

Fast And Slow

The old crow is getting slow.
   The young crow is not.
Of what the young crow does not know
   The old crow knows a lot.

At knowing things the old crow
   Is still the young crow's master.
What does the slow old crow not know?
   — How to go faster.

The young crow flies above, below,
   And rings around the slow old crow.
What does the fast young crow not know?
   — Where to go.

How Much Is A Gross?

Here come a dozen kangaroos
Wearing a gross of tennis shoes.
How many is a gross? Don't guess.
A gross is not a more-or-less.
It is precisely an amount.
If you don't know, I'll help you count.

To start with, you must realize
Few kangaroos can find their size
In tennis shoes. They have to put
Six of the things on either foot
To get one big enough. They rip them
Front and back, and then they slip them,
Six on the left, six on the right,
Then get some string and tie them tight.
Then slap the ground and off they thump,
Six shoes to a thumper, twelve to a jump.
Multiply by twelve kangaroos
And that's a gross of tennis shoes.

Sylvester

Sylvester wrote to Mary Lou.
Said, "Will you marry me?"
Replied a Lady Kangaroo,
"My darling, I agree."

"Agree to what?" Sylvester cried.
"I've never before seen *you!*"
"Well, no," the Kangaroo replied,
"But though *that's* perfectly true,

Here is your letter sent to me."
"To *you!* Don't be absurd!"
"Don't tamper with the mails," said she,
"A man must keep his word!"

"My letter was sent to Mary Lou!"
"It came to *me!*" "Agreed.
But you saw it wasn't addressed to you!"
"How could I? — I can't read."

"Then how could you read the letter
But not how it was addressed?"
"I could say your writing got better,
Or I could say I just guessed.

The point is," said the Kangaroo,
" — And the mailman will agree —
Whatever you wrote to Mary Lou,
The letter came to *me.*

You must either learn to write what you mean
Or to mean what you write!" she cried.
"And though I'd rather not make a scene,
I insist you must make me your bride!"

"We'll just see about that," said Sylvester. "No doubt
We will," said the Kangaroo.
— And how do you think it all turned out?
— I only wish I knew.

There Was A Hunter From Littletown

There once was a Hunter from Littletown.
    He made his bullets of sugar cane.
And every duck that he shot down
    Got up and flew away again.

He shot a Lobster out of a tree
    And up it rose again and said:
"Sorry. Which way is the sea?"
    Said the Hunter: "Aren't you dead?"

"Dead?" said the Lobster. "What a thought!
    Why ever should I be dead?"
"I'm sure," said the Hunter, "I heard a shot.
    Would you look for a hole in your head?"

"Do you call that polite?" the Lobster replied.
    "I'll thank you to be more agreeable."
But he put up one claw to his forehead and cried:
    "Oh really, *this* wasn't foreseeable!"

For there *was* a hole, and however he tried
    He couldn't deny it. "Oh mercy on me!"
Wept the Lobster, and promptly rolled over and died.
    Said the Hunter: "You're kind to agree."

And that night at supper his wife picked a claw
    And the Hunter at least two or three,
From the finest fat Lobster that ever you saw
    Shot down from its perch in a tree.

Children When They're Very Sweet

Children, when they're very sweet,
    Only bite and scratch and kick
A very little. Just enough
    To show their parents they're not sick.

After all if children *should*
    (By some horrible mistake)
Be entirely good all day
    Every parent's heart would ache.

"Our little monsters must be ill:
    They're much too well behaved!
Call the doctor! Do it quick!
    Maybe they can still be saved!

...Wait! They're looking better now.
    Johnny just kicked Billy's shin!
Betty just bit Teddy's ear!
    Jane just stuck me with a pin!

There! The little dears are fit
    As sharks and crocodiles, you'll find.
No need for the doctor now:
    Get a stick and make them mind!"

The Happy Family

Before the children say goodnight,
    Mother, Father, stop and think:
Have you screwed their heads on tight?
    Have you washed their ears with ink?

Have you said and done and thought
    All that earnest parents should?
Have you beat them as you ought?
    Have you begged them to be good?

And above all—when you start
    Out the door and douse the light—
Think, be certain, search your heart:
    Have you screwed their heads on tight?

If they sneeze when they're asleep,
    Will their little heads come off?
If they just breathe very deep?
    If—especially—they cough?

Should—alas—the little dears
    Lose a little head or two,
Have you inked their little ears:
    Girls' ears pink and boys' ears blue?

Children's heads are very loose.
    Mother, Father, screw them tight.
If you feel uncertain use
    A monkey wrench, but do it right.

If a head should come unscrewed
    You will know that you have failed.
Doubtful cases should be glued.
    Stubborn cases should be nailed.

Then when all your darlings go
        Sweetly screaming off to bed,
Mother, Father, you may know
        Angels guard each little head.

Come the morning you will find
        One by one each little head
Full of gentle thoughts and kind,
        Sweetly screaming to be fed.

What You Will Learn About The Brobinyak

The Brobinyak has Dragon Eyes
And a tail the shape of a Fern
And teeth about Banana Size,
As one day you may learn
If ever you sail across the Sea
On the Shell of a Giant Clam
And come to the Forest of Foofenzee
In the Land of the Pshah of Psham.

There is no language he can't speak
And you may, if you please,
Be swallowed whole in French or Greek,
Or nibbled in Chinese.
And once inside the Brobinyak
You'll meet a lot of friends:
The Three-Toed Gleep and the Saginsack
And a covey of Two-Tailed Bends.

The Russian Bear is always there,
    And Glocks from the Polar Sea.
And Radio Eels with static squeals,
    And the Piebald Peccary.
The Splinterwave from his Ocean Cave
    Will greet you at the door.
And the Green Kilkenny collect your penny
    And pitch it along the floor.
The Banjo Tern and the Fiddling Hern
    Will play you a Wedding March.
But keep your eye on the Lullaby
    Or he'll nibble your collar for starch.
Oh keep your eye on the Lullaby
    And never speak to the Mullet,
Or the Scrawny Shank will leave his Tank
    And nibble you quick as a bullet.
And never look at the Seven-Nosed Hook
    Or, with a frightful roar,
He'll sniff enough of his Pepper Snuff
    To sneeze you out the door.

What You Will Learn About The Brobinyak   Robert J. Byrd

Oh the Brobinyak has Dragon Eyes
And a tail the shape of a Fern
And teeth about Banana Size,
As one day you may learn
If ever you sail across the Sea
On the Shell of a Giant Clam
And come to the Forest of Foofenzee
In the Land of the Pshah of Psham.

Halloween

Ruth says Apples have learned to bob.
Bob says Pumpkins have a job.
      Here's the man from the Witching Tree.
      Ask *him* since you won't ask me:
Do you think Ruth is telling the truth?

"Man from the Tree, your skin is green.
What night is this?" "It's Halloween."

Ruth, Ruth, you told the truth.
The man says Apples *have* learned to bob.
The man says Pumpkins *do* have a job.
The man come down from the Witching Tree
Says he wants someone. No, not me.
Says he wants someone good and true —
          YOU!

Mother, Mother, Ruth's gone flying!
Hush, children, stop that crying.

Mother, Mother, she's up in The Tree!
Climb up and tell me what you see.

Mother, she's higher than I can climb!
She'll be back by breakfast time.

Mother, what if she's gone for good?
She'll have to make do with the witches' food.

Mother, what do witches eat?
Milk and potatoes and YOU, my sweet.

The River Is A Piece Of Sky

From the top of a bridge
The river below
Is a piece of sky —
            Until you throw
            A penny in
            Or a cockleshell
            Or a pebble or two
            Or a bicycle bell
            Or a cobblestone
            Or a fat man's cane —
And then you can see
It's a river again.

The difference you'll see
When you drop your penny:
The river has splashes,
The sky hasn't any.

The River Is A Piece Of Sky

Robert J. Byrd

How To Tell The Top Of A Hill

The top of a hill
Is not until
The bottom is below.
And you have to stop
When you reach the top
For there's no more UP to go.

To make it plain
Let me explain:
The one *most* reason why
You have to stop
When you reach the top — is:
The next step up is sky.

Summer Song

By the sand between my toes,
By the waves behind my ears,
By the sunburn on my nose,
By the little salty tears
That make rainbows in the sun
When I squeeze my eyes and run,
By the way the seagulls screech,
Guess where I am? *At the.....!*
By the way the children shout
Guess what happened? *School is.....!*
By the way I sing this song
Guess if summer lasts too long:
You must answer Right or.....!

Pennies From Heaven   Robert J. Byrd

Pennies From Heaven

There once was a jack on a steeple.
    He was painting it copper brown.
He dribbled paint on the people
    On the sidewalk eight flights down.

They thought it was raining pennies.
    They ran for their piggy banks.
And whenever they caught a drop in the slot
    They shouted, "Many thanks!"

Whenever they caught a drop in the slot
    They dreamed of what they would buy.
But they cried a lot, for they often got
    A drop or two in the eye.

They cried even more when they went to the store
    With their money and tried to spend it.
But it helps to cry when there's paint in your eye.
    And the steeple does look splendid!

He Lived, Alas, In A House Too Big

There was a man who lived in a house
  A big White House with a fence around it.
He lost his way from room to room,
  And nobody ever found it.

He picked up the phone and called the police.
  "Please come to my house and find me."
"Where are you?" they said. "I'm in one of my rooms
  With the rest in front and behind me.

"I'm in one of my rooms on one of my floors
  With the rest in front or behind me,
Except for those above and below.
  If fifty men can't find me."

"Send fifty more. I'll phone the cook
  To feed them pork and beans.
If you haven't found me by New Year's Day,
  I'll phone for the Horse Marines."

That was in January, I think,
  About three years ago.
A hundred police and the Horse Marines
  Ate up ten tons or so

Of pork and beans, then ten tons more.
  And twenty of pancake pie.
The horses ate forty tons of oats.
  The cook began to cry.

The man kept phoning from room to room.
  The cook kept phoning the store,
Said the man on the phone, "Have you found me yet?"
  Said the cook, "Send ten tons more."

Said the hundred police and the Horse Marines
  Whenever they answered the phone,
"Can you look around and see where you are?"
  Said the man, "I am here, and alone."

They finished the pork. They finished the beans.
   They finished the cook — she quit.
Now the phone keeps ringing in her room
   But nobody answers it.

A hundred police and the Horse Marines
   Are running around and around
Looking for something else to eat.
   And there's nothing to be found.

Not pork and beans. Not pancake pie.
   Not a cup of dishwater tea.
Not even the man they came to find
   Whoever he may be.

If he ever turns up from wherever he is
   In the big White House with the fence around it,
He is in there yet, but he lost his way
   And nobody ever found it.

The Dollar Dog

I had a dollar dog named Spot.
He wasn't much, but he was a lot
Of *kinds* of dog, plus a few parts flea,
Seven parts yapper, and seventy-three
Or seventy-four parts this-and-that.
The only thing he wasn't was cat.
He was collie-terrier-spaniel-hound
And everything else they have at the pound.
Yes, some might call him a mongrel, but
To me he was thoroughbred, pedigreed mutt.
A middle-sized nothing, or slightly smaller,
But a lot of kinds to get for a dollar.

The Lesson

Of all the fleas that ever flew
(And flying fleas are rather few
((Because for proper flying you
(((Whether you are a flea or not)))
Need wings and things fleas have not got))) —

(I make the further point that fleas
Are thick as these parentheses
((An illustration (((you'll agree)))
Both apt and pleasing to a flea))) —

Now then where were we? Let me see —
Ah, yes. — We said to fly you ought
(Whether you are a flea or not)
To have some wings (yes, at least two
((At least no less than two will do
(((And fleas have something less than one
((((One less, in fact (((((or, frankly, none)))))
((((((Which, as once more you will agree))))))
Limits the flying of a flea)))))))))).

And let me add that fleas that fly
are known as Flears. (You can see why.)

All I have said thus far is true.
(If it's not clear, that's up to you.
((You'll have to learn sometime, my dear,
That what is true may not be clear
(((While what is clear may not be true
((((And you'll be wiser when you do.))))))))))

How I Helped The Traveler

Main Street? Yessir. Let me see —
If it isn't this street, it must be
The next or the next on the left or right.
Just go down here to the traffic light
And take a turn, or go straight ahead.
(You have to stop if the light is red.)
—That could be Main. If it's not Main,
Go round the block and try again.
You just can't miss it. It's in plain sight:
Straight ahead, or left, or right.

Margaret Nash Got Wet
But I Don't Know How

Margaret Nash
Went swimming — splash! —
Right in the middle of the Ocean.
"What? Swimming where?
Who took her there?"
— I haven't the slightest notion.

She jumped from a ship
And cut her lip
According to the Squid.
She fell from a plane
That was going to Spain.
That's what Fish say she did.

She fell from a cloud
She wasn't allowed —
Except in dreams — to ride.
It changed to rain
And she couldn't remain.
Or so I'm told by the Tide.

She paddled on toast
Away from the coast
According to the Whale.
The toast soaked thin.
Margaret fell in.
— But what an unlikely tale!

What a pack of lies;
It's just not wise
To trust what you hear in the Ocean.
And truth to tell
The fact is — well,
I haven't the slightest notion.

Captain Spud And His First Mate, Spade

Tough Captain Spud and his First Mate, Spade,
  Were saltier than most.
They followed the sea (that being their trade)
  From coast to coast to coast.

From coast to coast to coast is about
  As far as a sea can reach.
Once you sail in, you have to sail out,
  Or you'll be on the beach.

Not Spud and Spade. They made their trade
  Wherever they happened to be.
And just as soon as the trade was made
  They put back out to sea.

And once they were safely under way
  They'd start a squabble or two
To pass the hours of the lonely day,
  As good friends often do.

They sailed with a cargo of Yo-yo strings
  Hand-woven in the Highlands,
And traded for bottle caps and things
  In the far-off Sandbox Islands.

They sailed to where the Gum Trees grow
  And traded the caps for prizes:
Tin whistles, jacks, and balls of wax,
  And ten-for-a-penny surprises.

Said Spud to Spade as they loaded the hold,
  "Some swindler in this crew
Has swiped my genuine plastic-gold
  Space Badge—and I mean you!"

Said Spade to Spud, "You're much too quick
  With your fingers. That ball of twine,
And seven feet of the licorice stick
  You have in your pocket are mine!"

Captain Spud And His First Mate, Spade   Charles H. Waterhouse

Said Spud, "I have eyes in the back of my head,
    And I'm watching you, old mate-oh!"
"That's how it is, old Spud," Spade said,
    When your head is a potato.

"It has eyes in front that cannot see.
    And eyes in back that are blind.
And nothing inside, as it seems to me,
    That might pass for half a mind."

And so, as good friends often do.
    They bickered night and day,
And treated themselves to a squabble or two
    To pass the lonely day.

So they grew rich in the Yo-yo trade,
    And testier than most.
—As you'll hear men say of Spud and Spade
    In the jungle gyms of the Coast.

For Spud was a salt, and Spade was a tar.
    And both were sea-going men.
Till they took to going to sea so far
    They never were heard of again.

All I Did Was Ask My Sister A Question

Why is water wet?   Let's see —
Because...   Well, silly, it has to be!
How could you drink it if it were dry?
If you got a drop of it in your eye
It would sting like sand and make you cry.
When it started to rain, it would come down dust.
You'd have to hold your breath till you bust
Or turn to powder inside your chest.
And how would I pass my swimming test
And get my badge?   Not that you'd care.
You'd still be standing around somewhere
Asking foolish questions to get me mad!
Well, I'll tell Mother and she'll tell Dad.
Then see what he does to you for that!
And see if I care, you little brat!

Why Nobody Pets The Lion At The Zoo

The morning that the world began
The Lion growled a growl at Man.

And I suspect the Lion might
(If he'd been closer) have tried a bite.

I think that's as it ought to be
And not as it was taught to me.

I think the Lion has a right
To growl a growl and bite a bite.

And if the Lion bothered Adam,
He should have growled right back at 'im.

The way to treat a Lion right
Is growl for growl and bite for bite.

True, the Lion is better fit
For biting than for being bit.

But if you look him in the eye
You'll find the Lion's rather shy.

He really wants someone to pet him.
The trouble is: his teeth won't let him.

He has a heart of gold beneath
But the Lion just can't trust his teeth.

Why Nobody Pets The Lion At The Zoo   Charles H. Waterhouse

The Blabberhead

The Blabberhead is blubbery.
His face is full of shrubbery.
His neck is long and rubbery.

So is his nose. That nose of his
Is blue and sticks out of his fizz
Into whatever's not his biz —

I mean his *business*. What is not
His business is, well, quite a lot.
In fact, most everything. But wot —

I mean *what* makes the Blabber one
Most systematically to shun
Is that the instant he is done

Sticking his nose into affairs
He sticks it out again, and stares,
And gives himself all sorts of airs.

Then, grabbing everyone's lapel,
He starts to tell and tell and tell.
Worse yet, he doesn't tell it well.

He blabbers, blubbers, blurts, and fizzes.
He rattles off the that's and this's.
Whatever business isn't his is

All his business. In he charges
Like a river full of barges,
And (to say the least) enlarges

On whatever he can pick up.
Then, as like as not, he'll hiccup
Eat your cake, and break the teacup,

While that bright blue nose of his,
Sticking out of his mad fizz,
Sniffs so that it makes you diz —

I mean *dizzy*. Yammer, clatter!
Here he is! There goes the platter!
Here comes gossip—splutter, splatter!

You can see from what I've said
The manners of the Blabberhead
Are of a sort you well may dread.

Avoid, abstain from, shun, eschew
False blabbering (or even true),
Or you may soon discover *you*

Are growing loud and blubbery
With a face all full of shrubbery,
And a neck too long and rubbery,

And (as your nose turns blue)
That a universal snubbery
Will certainly ensue.

Widgeonry

Charles H. Waterhouse

Widgeonry
(And Why *Shouldn't* You Use Your Dictionary?)

A widgeon in a wicopy
In which no widgeon ought to be
A widowed widgeon was.

While in a willow wickiup
A Wichitaw sat down to sup
With other Wichitaws.

And what they whittled as they ate
Included what had been of late
A widgeon's wing. 'Twas thus

The widgeon in the wicopy
In which no widgeon ought to be
A widowed widgeon was.

Speed Adjustments

A man stopped by and he wanted to know
Why my son John had become so slow.

I looked out the window and there was John,
Running so fast he had come and gone
Before I saw him. "Look at him go!"
I said to the man. "Do you call *that* slow?"

"He seems to be fast when he wants to be,"
The man agreed. "It would seem to me
He is one of those two-speed boys. You know—
Sometimes fast and sometimes slow.
He runs a mile in nothing flat.
He can run right out from under his hat
When there's nowhere, really, to go. But yet,
Why does a boy who's fast as a jet
Take all day—and sometimes two—
To get to school? I'm sure that you
Send him to school. But yesterday
He didn't get there. And all he would say
When I asked why, was: he started at eight,
But it took so long he got there late."

"How late?" said I.
                        Said the man, "A day."

"I see," said I, "and I think I may say
He won't be late again. He needs
A little adjustment of his speeds,
And I'm sure I know the place to adjust."

"Well, then, that's that," said he. "I must
Be on my way."
                        "Thank you," said I.
"If you see John as you go by
Would you be so good as to send him in?
There is never a better time to begin
A speed adjustment than right away."

"Agreed, and I will," said the man. "Good day."

And just a few minutes after that
In came John and down he sat:
"You wanted to see me, I understand."

"I did, and I do. But you'll have to stand—
At least at first—for what I need,"
Said I, "for I have to adjust your speed.
And when I'm through adjusting it,
I think you won't much care to sit.
Do you know what I mean?"
                                        "Oh, oh," said he.
"I'm afraid I do. Is it going to be
Terribly long before you're through?"

"Why, not at all," said I. "Like you,
I can be speedy sometimes, too."

And soon after that, his speeds were adjusted.
And also the seat of his pants was dusted.
It was busy work, but it didn't take long,
And I double-checked as I went along,
Just to make sure there was nothing wrong.

And whatever *was* wrong, I set it straight.
For since that time he hasn't been late.

The Lesson For Tonight
Which Is: When You Do Things, Do Them Right.
Above All, Try To Be Polite.

When you are at the table
    And you need to kick your brother,
Be as sweet as you are able
    To your Dad and Mother.

Thank them for the lovely food
    In a pleasant voice, and — quick! —
While you're being very good,
    That's the time to kick!

When your brother starts to cry
    Always say — *and do not grin
As you say it* — "My, oh my!
    Did I bump your little shin?"

Dad and Mother, you will find,
    Will say you did just right,
And tell your brother he should mind
    His manners and be more polite.

Now, what's the lesson for tonight?
    Right! *Don't let your badness show!*
Above the table be polite.
    Be yourself below.

Then, when you grow up and find
    People run from you at sight,
You may, for your peace of mind,
    Know you've always been polite.

Evan Kirk

Evan Kirk
Is looking for work.
Work? What can he do?
He could milk a cow
If he just knew how.
He can almost buckle a shoe.

He can count to ten
Again and again
With hardly a real mistake.
He could drive a bus
If one of us
Would handle the wheel and the brake.

He can climb a chair
When no one's there
And reach where the cookies are.
He can catch you frogs
And pollywogs
At eleven cents a jar.

For a nickel a day
He will hammer away
At woodwork, walls, and doors.
Or for nothing at all
He will paint the hall
And nail down all your floors.

The little dear
Has been working here
A year — well, almost two.
And you couldn't foresee
How glad we'd be
To send him to work on you.

The Monster Den

I met your Mummy long ago.
She said, "How do you do?" I said, "Hello!"
And we talked a little about a lot.
And as we talked we sat and thought
A lot or a little. And then, I guess,
I asked her a question, and she said, "Yes."
And what I asked was — let me see —
It must have been "Will you marry me?"
For that's what she did. And I married *her*
With a church and a cake and a ring.

                                     Well, sir,
We left our friends when the cake was gone.
We kept the ring (she has it on)
And we changed our clothes and we took a train
To somewhere, I think. And then a plane
To somewhere else.

                      We thought we were
Living happily ever after, sir,
As the stories say. We didn't know then
We were only starting a MONSTER DEN.
But that's what we did.

                        We had it in mind
To have some children. The human kind
Was what we intended. And I will say
It almost started out that way.

For Monster One was pink as a rose
And looked like a girl, with a button nose,
And giggly eyes, and a crookedy smile.
So we called her Myra — for a while.
And then what happened? She grew and grew
And after a while there was no one but YOU
Where our baby had been.

                        As for Monster Two,
He looked like a boy, so we called him John.
How could we know what was going on?
He looked like a boy, and a fine one, too.
So we took him home. And he grew and grew.

But he hadn't grown much before we knew
What *looked* like a boy was really YOU!

Mummy cried and hung her head.
"Someone is monstering us!" she said.
"Our house is becoming a Monster Den!"

But we didn't give up. We tried again.
And that time what we got was — Benn!
Yes, YOU! — and were we happy then?

Well, all I shall say is that made three.
And I looked at Mummy and she looked at me.
And we looked again at what we had got.
And we thought a little about a lot
As we took it home. For we knew right then
It isn't really a Monster Den
Until you have at least one Benn!

So there we were with our Monsters Three
Breathing out fire at Mummy and me.

And what did we do? What would *you* do?
Right!
        We turned into Monsters, too!

Mummy Slept Late And Daddy Fixed Breakfast............

Daddy fixed the breakfast
He made us each a waffle.
It looked like gravel pudding
It tasted something awful.

"Ha Ha," he said. "I'll try again.
This time I'll get it right."
But what *I* got was in between
Bituminous and anthracite.

"A little too well done? Oh well,
I'll have to start all over."
That time what landed on my plate
Looked like a manhole cover.

I tried to cut it with a fork,
The fork gave off a spark.
I tried a knife and twisted it
Into a question mark.

I tried it with a hack-saw.
I tried it with a torch.
It didn't even make a dent.
It didn't even scorch.

The next time Dad gets breakfast
When Mommy's sleeping late,
I think I'll skip the waffles,
I'd sooner eat the plate!

Mummy Slept Late And Daddy Fixed Breakfast   Lonni Sue Johnson

Friendship

Willy the Weep and Sad Terry and I
Were sitting here thinking of you.
And Willy and Terry were having a cry.
And I was having one, too, I was.
For we knew it just had to be true, we did.
We knew it just had to be true.

Willy had hot dogs and Terry had toast
And I had a pail full of lunch.
But our tears came so hard and so fast (almost)
We sat there and just couldn't munch. (Not quite,
But *almost* we just couldn't munch.) Besides,
The tears were wetting our lunch.

Said Willy the Weep as he chewed and he cried,
"I cannot believe it is true!"
And Sad Terry said, "Pass the salt." And he sighed,
"I hate to believe it myself, I do. (Except
That, of course, it is perfectly true. Too bad.
But we all know it's perfectly true.)"

So I ate a pickle and Willy the Weep
Ate six and Sad Terry ate ten.
And we wept and we ate till we all fell asleep
In our sorrow, and oh, even then (alas)
We wept for you now and again, we did,
Till we woke and wept for you again.

"But (please pass the mustard) just what did he do?"
Said Terry, "I have to agree
That whatever it was must be perfectly true,
Though I hate to believe it, for he (poor boy)
Is my friend. But, of course, I'll agree, I will,
If you will explain it to me."

"Oh, a terrible thing," said Willy, "and that
Is the whole truth. A terrible shame.
Though now that you ask, I don't know just what.
But a terrible thing all the same (I'm sure).
And though it's a terrible shame, I say,
He'll just have to shoulder the blame."

So Willy the Weep and Sad Terry and I
Were speaking in friendship of you.
And Willy and Terry were having a cry.
And I was having one, too, I was.
For we knew it just had to be true, we did.
We knew it just had to be true.

A Fine Fat Fireman   Lonni Sue Johnson

A Fine Fat Fireman

A fine fat fireman ran up the ladder.
  He blew out the fire with a fine fat puff.
He reached for the lady. He almost had 'er
  When the ladder decided enough was enough.

Snap went the first rung. *Snap* went the second.
  Down came the fireman, fine and fat.
He landed on the chief. The chief hadn't reckoned
  On anything as fine and as fat as that.

Down flew the lady. She lost a slipper
  And three gold pins when she landed in the net.
Down slid the fireman like the handle of a zipper.
  The chief lost his ladder. (He hasn't fixed it yet.)

Down went the chief with his helmet dented.
  He woke with the fireman sitting on his head.
He spoke to the fireman. They haven't yet invented
  All of the words for what he said.

Some of his words had sparks at the center.
  They floated up the wall—floated higher and higher.
They reached the lady's window. The lady saw them enter.
  Half a minute later they restarted the fire!

Up jumped the fireman, fine and fat.
  He climbed the wall. He puffed out the blaze.
The lady kissed the fireman. "A man like that
  Is the man for me for the rest of my days!"

The chief fired the fireman. The fireman quit.
  "Huff and puff for yourself," said he.
"This work's too hot by more than a bit."
  And he married the lady and he went to sea.

Now he's a sailor, a fine fat salt.
  The lady has new gold pins. (Slippers, too.)
If your helmet's dented it's your own foolish fault.
  Don't stand under ladders. You'll be sorry if you do.

I Hate To Wait

Someone came to see me when I was not at home.
I let him in and told him I was sorry he had come
On just exactly almost the day I wasn't there.
So we made an appointment to meet again somewhere.
I think we said last Tuesday noon at quarter after eight.
He said he'd be there on the dot but that he might be late.
I said if he was there on time I would be glad to wait.
I even told my mother I was going to meet him there.
But now it's Thursday morning and I can't remember where
I was supposed to meet him. I know he hasn't come.
I'll give him ten more minutes. And then I'm going home.

Time

The stars sit still and the world goes round —
India, Egypt, U.S.A. —
The world keeps turning, the sun comes out.
And that's the story of every day.

Turn from the East, turn to the West,
The sun comes out and starts to climb
As high as noon, then down again.
And that's the story of time.

The stars tell time to the telescope.
The telescope tells the clock.
The clock tells everyone in the house.
And that's the story of tick and tock.

If you want to hear the star in the clock
Go fish one out of the pool.
If you can't do that, you'll have to wait
Till you learn the stars in school.

But the truth is just what I said it was,
And just as it has to be,
And just as it always was before,
And just as they taught it to me —

The stars tell time to the telescope,
And the telescope tells the clock,
And the clock tells everyone in the house.
And that's the story of tick and tock.

Rain Sizes

Lonni Sue Johnson

Rain Sizes

Rain comes in various sizes.
Some rain is as small as a mist.
It tickles your face with surprises,
And tingles as if you'd been kissed.

Some rain is the size of a sprinkle
And doesn't put out all the sun.
You can see the drops sparkle and twinkle,
And a rainbow comes out when it's done.

Some rain is as big as a nickle
And comes with a crash and a hiss.
It comes down too heavy to tickle.
It's more like a splash than a kiss.

When it rains the right size and you're wrapped in
Your rainclothes, it's fun out of doors.
But run home before you get trapped in
The big rain that rattles and roars.

On Going To Hohokus
(And Why I Live In New Jersey)

From Peapack to Hohokus
  Is really not too far
Unless you start from somewhere else.
  It depends on where you are.

I went from Lower Squankum once
  Through Bacon's Neck and Hopatcong
With a stop at Cheesequake, but I think
  That way's a bit too long.

It's longer from Piscataway
  Across to Tuckahoe
With a detour through Buckshutum.
  Still, the main thing is to go.

And if you really don't know why
  But somehow feel you should,
Wear tight shoes: when you take them off,
  Your feet will feel so good.

You can't help being happy there,
  Though when you think about
Having to start back, you may wish
  You hadn't started out.

I Am Writing This At Sea

I met your father yesterday. He asked me what I thought
About the price of lettuce seed. (It has gone up a lot.)
He asked if I liked baked beans cold. (I certainly do not.)
He told me he had some for sale and if I liked them hot
He would be more than happy to sell me a bean pot.

I told him I had two at home and one aboard my yacht.
That brought us round to sailing, a subject that soon brought
The talk around to fishing and the big ones we had caught.
And after we had lied a bit (as fishermen will do)
We found we had no more to say, and so we talked of you.

I told him you were very good when you were good at all.
He shook his head and sighed and said he couldn't quite recall
The last time you were any good except that week last fall
When you were home in bed with grippe. I said I'd heard you bawl
When you had to take your medicine. He said, in general,
He'd rather row an elephant to Salem in a squall
Than put up with your antics when you start to caterwaul.
But we agreed you eat quite well, and that when you were small
You weren't as wide as you are now, nor — certainly — as tall.
That left us with no more to say, and so, as usual,
I bought my beans, put them aboard, and sailed off with the tide.
And he cast off my lines for me, and then went home and cried.

And Here's What Happened Next
or
Those Three

Miss Myra and Small Benn and John L. — those three —
Grew tired of Mummy, grew tired of me,
Grew tired of manners, of baths, and of bed,
And of having to mind us whatever we said
(Which they never did, where they always went late,
Which they never took, which were bad when they ate.)

Which is to say, they meant to be rid
Of a lot of things they never did
(Or never on time, or never right)
And so they ran away one night.

They left us a note and in it they said:
"Minding and manners and baths and bed
Have ruined our lives. We are running away.
Good-bye. There is nothing more to say."

And they signed it and left. And so they were rid
Of all those things they never did
(Or never right, or never on time).
Small Benn took a quarter, Miss Myra a dime,
And John L. (who never could save) one cent.
And they bought their tickets and off they went.

They wrote us from Spain, but they sent no news.
They wrote us from Egypt and asked for shoes
(Which we sent them at once, for well we knew
How the hot sand burns when your shoes wear through).

They wrote us from India next to say
How happy they were they had run away.
"We are seeing the world! It is good to be rid
Of all those things we never did —
Minding and manners and baths and bed.
Small Benn has warts. Miss Myra's head
Is full of wool. John L. just said
All the bad words he was never allowed

To use at home. (My, he looks proud!)
And none of us ever mind anymore.
And we drop our things all over the floor.
And we never ever go to bed.
Well, thanks for the shoes." — That's what they said
In the note from India.

Their last note
(It was the last good-bye they wrote
As far as we know) was marked "At Sea."
And what it said was: "Since we're free,
We're bound for Australia. That's where we'll be
By the time this letter gets to you.
We are going to catch us a Kangaroo.
Please send us at once a Kangaroo Trap,
Some Pretzels and Pickles, and maybe a Map
With the Kangaroo Places marked in red,
And a Ball of Twine, and a Spool of Thread
(John L. has a rip, and Small Benn's kite
Is out of String). We are all right.
I hope you are sorry we ran away."
It was signed "Miss Myra," and dated "May."

We sent the Twine for Small Benn's kite
Air-parcel-post that very night,
With a Spool of Thread (and a Needle, too,)
For John L.'s rip. But the best I could do
With the Kangaroo Map was a bit of a mess.
I didn't know, so I had to guess
Where the Kangaroo Places were likely to be,
And *all* of Australia looked likely to me,
And even some parts of Alaska and Texas.
Before I was through, there were so many X's
They covered the map so, that no one could tell
What it was a map *of*. I did do quite well
With the Pretzels and Pickles (one tub and one barrel)
Which I wrapped in odd bits of Miss Myra's apparel.
(She had left things behind — in her hurry perhaps.)
So that much was done. But the Kangaroo Traps! —

Oh, those Kangaroo Traps! Have any of *you*
Tried shopping for things that might possibly do
For catching and holding a live Kangaroo?
I finally bought a large cage at the zoo.
At least that would *hold* one, though I couldn't guess
How it might *trap* it—and couldn't care less.

We wrapped it all up. It made quite a pack,
So we sent *that* by ship.

                 In three years it came back
With a letter that read:
                "Dear Mr. and Mrs.:
By official report (and that is what this is)
Miss Myra and Small Benn and John L.—those three
Have been here and gone. As it seems now to me
They will not be back, as I think you'll agree.
The details are as follows:
                  Small Benn: lost at sea.
Sailed off in a tantrum, split up on a reef.
Some think he attacked it. We share your great grief.

The one called Miss Myra (as far as we know)
Lies buried in ninety-nine inches of snow.
Report states that though it was starting to blow
She went out to buy pickles at forty-below.
We repeat our condolences.

                 That leaves—let's see—
The one called John L. As sworn before me
By rumor and hearsay and witnesses, he
Did say his bad words to a King Kangaroo
That replied with a kick that would certainly do
To put him in orbit, and certainly did.
Once more—our regrets. Postage due, seven quid.
I am, sir and madam, John Jasper MacNeice,
House Painter, Gents' Tailor, and Chief of Police."

We read it straight through, and again, and again

(Once backwards, and once in a mirror) and then,
I looked at Mummy and she looked at me.
And that's when we knew that at last we were free
Of Miss Myra and Small Benn and John L. — those three.
But we fought back our tears and our sorrow, we did.
I counted my money and sent seven quid
(That's twenty-one dollars) to J. J. MacNeice,
House Painter, Gents' Tailor, and Chief of Police.
And Mummy replied with a courteous note,
Taking pains (for politeness) to say that he wrote
A most elegant hand, and she thanked him for that.
And when she was finished, I put on my hat.
And she put on hers. And in silence we two
Walked out through the park, down those paths we both knew,
And — still silent — we paused half a day at the zoo.
For it brought back fond memories — to her and to me —
Of Miss Myra and Small Benn and John L. — those three.

Time Leaves No Time When You're A Boy

Just being a boy takes all (about)
Of every day and half the night
Hurrying off, on, by, in, out,
Near, far, around, through, left, and right.

Learning never to say *please*,
Yessir, thank you, how are you?
Leaves little time for climbing trees,
Egg throwing, and things you *have* to do.

Put yourself in a boy's shoes —
Remember (or shall I remind you?)
It takes time to learn to lose
Things when they're right behind you,
Close a door so that it blows
Half off its hinges, never eat
Except between meals. Goodness knows,
That takes time. And, I repeat,
Time leaves no time as a boy grows.

And Here's What Happened Last
or
How Mummy And I Were Finally
Unmonstered Forever

It was seven slow years and three months—to the day—
When I looked at our sundial. It read HALF PAST MAY
Or TWO QUARTERS TO JUNE—whichever you choose.
For we *do* have a sundial, and sundials may use
Any language they please. (How else could they speak
To the Arab, the Chinese, the Finn, and the Greek
To tell them the time?)
                              And the time sundials tell
May be minutes and hours. But it may just as well
Be seconds and sparkles, or seasons and flowers.
No, don't think of time as just minutes and hours.
Time can be heartbeats, or bird songs, or miles,
Or waves on a beach, or ants in their files
(They *do* move like seconds—just watch their feet go:
Tick-tick-tick, like a clock). You'll learn as you grow
That whatever there is in a garden, the sun
Counts up on its dial. By the time it is done
Our sundial—or someone's—will certainly add
All the good things there are. Yes, and all of the bad.
And if anyone's here for the finish, the sun
Will have told him—by sundial—how well we have done.
How well we have done, or how badly. Alas,
That *is* a long thought. Let me hope we all pass.

Seven slow years had passed. Plus three months—to the day
Since Miss Myra, Small Benn, and John L. ran away.
And Mummy and I had had long thoughts to think.
With only two dishes at once in the sink,
The washing took no time, and wiping took less.
And with no one around to leave things in a mess
We had *time* for long thoughts. And the very long-longest,
And also the saddest, and also the strongest
Was—just as you've guessed (for what else could it be?)—
Of Miss Myra and Small Benn and John L.—those three.

But when you start thinking a very long thought

You will find, as a rule, that before you have got
Halfway to the end, you have thought yourself through
—To a nap.

     I was napping. And Mummy was, too.
When a rattle-bang-knock at the door broke our peace
—And there stood none other than J. J. MacNeice,
House Painter, Gents' Tailor, and Chief of Police.

"I have come, sir and madam," he said with a bow,
"To bring you some letters that reached me just now.
—Yes, that is rather fast. But the how and the why
Of it all is—I happened to be passing by.
I was out for a stroll, and the first thing I knew
I happened to find I was strolling by you
Which happened to bring to my mind certain metters"
(I think he meant "matters") "concerning three letters
I happened to have in my pocket, which I
Now place in your hand before going my why"
(I think he meant "way") "for I have—do you see?—
To hurry if I'm to get back home for tea."

"It *is* a long stroll," Mummy said. I agreed.
"May I say you have come with remarkable speed?"
I added politely. At which Mummy nodded
(For a pleasant remark really should be applauded.
If that's what you think, we're of one mind with you.
Though the rule to remember is: Don't Overdo).
"Do come in, sir," I said. Replied J. J. MacNeice,
Gents' Tailor, House Painter, and Chief of Police:
"I thank you, but, sadly, I'm forced to decline.
I've a fitting at seven, my dinner at nine,
Some painting to do after dinner, and then
Some police forms to fill out. My business has been
Rather brisk this past season. So if you'll allow,
I'll just leave these letters and start back right now."

—Which he did, after making an elegant bow.
Pausing only to say that the suit I had on

Was very well cut. And again — on the lawn —
To turn a professional eye on the house
And nod with approval and call back to us,
"That's a fine coat of paint!" (He *was* very polite.)

And with that he turned quickly and passed out of sight.
(I *do* hope he got to his fitting all right,
And had a good dinner, for after *that* stroll
He must have been ready to eat an ox whole!)

Well, I looked at Mummy and she looked at me
And we looked at the letters (of which there were three)
And a day and a night and an hour or two more
Flew by. And we still hadn't moved from the door
Nor opened the letters. We just didn't dare.
Till I heard Mummy say, "This will get us nowhere.
And it's starting to rain. Let me put on some tea
While you open the letters and read them to me."

And that's what we did. (She poured and I read.)
I opened the first. "It's from Myra," I said.

"Oh, good," Mummy answered. "With one lump or two?"
"Our — uh — daughter," I said. "I think one lump will do."
"There, now," Mummy said as she passed me my tray.
"Don't let it get cold. And what does she say?"

So I drank down my tea and I finished my bread
And I read her the letter, and here's what it said:

"Dear Mummy and Daddy: I think I've caught cold.
And, somehow or other, I think I've got old.
I went out for a walk — it seems ages ago —
And the first thing I knew it had started to snow.
And the next thing I knew I was standing — *kerchoo!* —
In a puddle of slush and was soaked through and through.
Please send me some stuff that is good for a sneeze."

(Here I looked at Mummy and said, "She said 'please'!"

But all Mummy said was, "What else does she need?
We'll discuss manners later. Right now—please—just read."
So I looked for my place and I started again
From—uh—"Good for a sneeze:")

                              "...And a dollar and ten
For a movie and pickles. Would you like to come?
If not, send my plane fare and I'll come straight home
Right after the feature the second time through.
It is, I am told, a fine picture—*kerchoo!*—
By the man who sells tickets, a J. J. MacNeice,
Theater Owner, Head Usher, and Chief of Police.
He also sells dresses—send money for two.
Well, that's all for now. I must close. How are you?
Love—Myra."

            The next was from John L. and read:
"Hi Earthlings! That comet you saw overhead
Was yours truly in orbit! I made it! Please send
Some money for food and some money to spend
And some money to have. Mr. J. J. MacNeice,
Travel Agent, Gents' Tailor, and Chief of Police
Is getting the tickets on Flight 93
And has made me a suit. I'll arrive C.O.D.
Pick me up at the airport—and bring a surprise.
Well, regards from the Space Kid to both of you guys.
Signed—Jon'l."

            I looked up at Mummy and said,
"Well, nothing has changed!" She nodded her head.
But all she would say was, "Read on." So I read.
The last letter, of course, was from Benn:

                              "Derest Ded:
I hev bin out two see an I gut my fete wett
But I will cum hom now as soone as I get
The mony you send me. Send it rite awai.
I do nut like geting wett evry dai.
It is two much like bathes. That is all. Yor sun Benn.
(An wen I gett hom plees do nut start agen
Abote bathing and minding and maners becuz

I do nut want things to get back like they wuz.
Luv to Momey. Make chek out to J. J. MacNees,
Shipp's Captin, Dri Guds, and Cheef of Polees.
I own him a debt for a tiket, yu see,
An sum close I wuz needing. Wel, goodby now — Me.")

—Well, I looked at Mummy a very long while.
And she looked at me. With no trace of a smile.
I said nothing to her. She said nothing to me.
An hour must have passed. And then two. And then three.
And then — still in silence — we started upstairs
And packed five valises — two of ours, three of theirs.
And we sent off the three care of J. J. MacNeice,
Miscellaneous Dealer and Chief of Police,
Along with a check that we thought ought to do.
And she got her coat. And I got mine, too.
And we both put them on. And also our hats.
And Mummy her fur piece. And I my best spats.
And I took our valises — one in each hand —
And we started to walk. And we walked. And walked. And
Then walked some more. Till we came to a train.
And got on. And
            WE NEVER
                    WERE HEARD
                            OF AGAIN.

About The Illustrators

Robert J. Byrd was born in Atlantic City, New Jersey in 1942 and educated at the Philadelphia Museum College of Art. He began his career as a studio illustrator but has been freelancing since 1969. The artist specialized in children's book illustration and was selected for the Junior Literary Guild in 1974-76. He has been included in exhibits of the World Children's Book Fair (Bologna, Italy), the Children's Book Showcase, the Children's Book Council, and his work for the Childcraft Encyclopedia (alphabet) is on permanent display at the Fields Enterprises Educational Corporation.

Mr. Byrd was honored with a one-man show at the Philadelphia Art Alliance and has been included in exhibits of the Philadelphia Art Directors Club, New York Art Directors Club, the Graphis Annual, and the Society of Illustrators. He has also shared his professional experience serving as a Professor at the Philadelphia College of Art and at Moore College of Art. He has resided for a number of years in Haddonfield, NJ.

Edward S. Gazsi, born in Trenton, New Jersey in 1944, resides in the rural community of New Egypt, NJ with his wife and four children. Working from a studio in his home, he has done illustrations for most of the major pharmaceutical advertising agencies in New York City and North Jersey. Since the beginning of his freelance career in 1971, his work has appeared regularly in several national periodicals.

Mr. Gazsi studied art at Cooper Union and Brooklyn College, where he had the opportunity to study with Philip Pearlstein. He is presently on the teaching staff of Mercer County Community College and has participated in the New Jersey State Teen Arts Festival as a workshop artist. A 1988 Gold Medal Winner in the Society of Illustrators' Annual Show, Edward Gazsi is frequently called upon to give lectures and demonstrations.

Lonni Sue Johnson was born in 1950 in Princeton, New Jersey where she attended school. She studied fine arts at the University of Michigan's School of Architecture and Design, receiving her BFA in 1972. She later attended the School of Visual Arts in New York City.

A prolific illustrator, Ms. Johnson has done drawings and illustrations for some of the most prominent publications in the country, including *The New Yorker*, *The New York Times*, *Fortune*, and *Business Week*, to name but a few. Her talents may also be seen in publications of IBM, the Museum of Modern Art, National Geographic Society and in the books of Harper & Row, Random House, Bantam, Simon & Schuster, among others.

Ms. Johnson's work has been recognized by the Society of Illustrators, Graphis, and the Society of Publication Design, and has appeared in the *American Illustration Annual*. She is included in the permanent collections of the Smithsonian Institution, the Princeton University Permanent Graphics Collection, the New Jersey State Museum, and Newark Museum.

Colonel Charles H. Waterhouse was educated at the Newark School of Fine and Industrial Art, and upon graduation served as staff artist with the Prudential Insurance Company before launching a freelance career. He spent the next 20 years drawing and painting covers and spreads for national magazines such as *Saga/Argosy*, *American Legion*, *Outdoor Life*, *Reader's Digest*, and numerous publications of the Boy Scouts of America.

He has served as combat artist for all four branches of the armed services, in Alaska, the United States and Vietnam. Three tours of Vietnam resulted in hundreds of works including publication of two books, *Vietnam Sketchbook — Delta to the DMZ*, and *Vietnam War Drawings: Air, Sea and Land*.

When the decision was made to produce a definitive history book on *Marines in the Revolution* for the Bicentennial, Colonel Waterhouse was chosen to do the illustration and recalled to active duty. He painted fourteen panels for the project, and his successful completion of the assignment brought an offer to continue painting the history of the USMC, and the treasured title of the first "artist-in-residence of the United States Marine Corps."

Colonel Waterhouse has been the subject of numerous articles and features in military, historical, and fine arts publications. His paintings are in the permanent collections of the Los Angeles Museum of National History, the Columbus Museum of Fine Arts, Prudential, Bell Telephone, Rutgers University, and all of the military art collections.

REGNERY/COWLES GED PROGRAM

INTERPRETATION OF READING MATERIALS IN THE NATURAL SCIENCES

Preparation for the High School Equivalency Examination

A COMPLETELY REVISED EDITION OF
READING COMPREHENSION IN THE
NATURAL SCIENCES

John T. Walsh, M.S.
Former Instructor in Biology, Delbarton School, Morristown, N.J.
Former Instructor in Mathematics, University of Notre Dame,
South Bend, Ind.

READING COMPREHENSION AND VOCABULARY SKILLS
by Judith Babbitts, B.A.
Reading Consultant, Executive Systems Corporation

COWLES BOOK COMPANY, INC.
A Subsidiary of Henry Regnery Company

Some of the material in this book was written by William R. Langner and Eric Foretich, and appeared in previous editions.

Special gratitude is extended to the noted science editor and author, Martin Keen, for his invaluable assistance in preparing the materials in this book.

Cowles Book Company, Inc.
A subsidiary of Henry Regnery Company
114 W. Illinois St., Chicago, Ill. 60610

Manufactured in the United States of America

Revised Edition

PREFACE

Interpretation of Reading Materials in the Natural Sciences has one purpose: to help you pass the "Interpretation of Reading Materials in the Natural Sciences" section of the General Educational Development (GED) Test, commonly called the High School Equivalency Examination.

This book is not just another question-and-answer book. It has been written with one examination in mind—the "Interpretation of Reading Materials in the Natural Sciences" section of the GED Test. Everything in this book reflects the latest developments in the GED Examination. The instructional material and the many practice exercises and tests will teach you the special skills necessary for reading and understanding written scientific material and scientific charts and diagrams. Also, you will learn how to make basic scientific calculations in several subjects. All practice exercises and tests contain the same kinds of questions that appear on the actual GED Science Test, and have fully explained answers. A special feature is a complete two-hour Simulated GED Science Examination which closely follows the content, form, and level of difficulty of the official GED Test.

The author of *Interpretation of Reading Materials in the Natural Sciences* is not only a specialist in his subject, but also in the GED Test. He has kept in mind at all times the special needs of GED students to help you acquire the knowledge and skills you need for passing the "Interpretation of Reading Materials in the Natural Sciences" section of the GED Test. Supplementing the author's own knowledge of the High School Equivalency Examination are numerous critical evaluations and many suggestions that have been painstakingly gathered from the best-qualified GED authorities in the country and from classroom teachers and students.

In order to be equally well prepared for the other four sections of the High School Equivalency Examination, you will want to study the other books in the Regnery/Cowles GED Program. Each reflects the latest developments in the official GED Examination and provides in-depth instruction in each specific subject area of the test. They are:

Correctness and Effectiveness of Expression. This volume provides you with instruction and drill in the fundamentals of English, including spelling, grammar and usage, and punctuation. Hundreds of practice exercises strengthen your skills in these areas. A two-hour Simulated GED English Usage Examination is included.

Interpretation of Reading Materials in the Social Studies. This volume presents a structured combination of instruction and drill in United

States and world history, economics, and other important social studies areas. Included are glossaries, a special section on interpreting maps and graphs, a chart of Highlights of United States Presidential Administrations, and a two-hour Simulated GED Social Studies Examination.

Interpretation of Literary Materials. This volume combines systematic instruction and drill in the interpretation of literary forms and devices which are important for understanding prose, poetry, and drama. It includes numerous reading exercises and a two-hour Simulated GED Literature Examination.

General Mathematical Ability. This specialized text provides you with comprehensive instruction and numerous practice exercises in many areas of mathematics, including fractions, algebra, geometry, and modern mathematics. It also includes a two-hour Simulated GED Mathematics Examination.

You may wish to supplement your study with an additional volume that treats all five subject areas of the test concisely with new material. It will be especially useful for extra practice.

Preparation for the High School Equivalency Examination (GED). This volume reflects the latest developments in the GED Test and provides instruction and drill in all five subject areas of the examination: English Usage, Social Studies, Science, Literature, and Mathematics. It contains a full ten-hour Simulated GED Test.

Many special features make each book a unique study tool for the examination. Each of the books contains a Diagnostic Test designed to pinpoint those areas in which you need further study. In addition, each volume contains instructional material and practice exercises with explanatory answers. These give you the practice essential for doing well on the Examination. And finally, each book, as described above, concludes with a unique Simulated GED Test. This test—patterned as closely as possible on the official examination or the section of it covered in that book—is designed to give you additional review and a "feel" for the real thing. It can be of major assistance to you in raising your score. For information about where to take the GED Test, check with your local high school or county or state department of education. A complete listing of state policies and addresses is included in the Appendix of *Preparation for the High School Equivalency Examination (GED)*.

The Editors

ACKNOWLEDGMENTS

Biological Sciences Curriculum Study: From *High School Biology, BSCS Green Version,* Rand McNally, Chicago, 1963.

Stewart M. Brooks: From *Basic Facts of General Chemistry,* by S. M. Brooks, copyright 1956. Reprinted by permission.

Cambridge Book Company, Inc.: From *Our Planet Earth,* copyright 1967 by Cambridge Book Company. Reprinted by permission of the publisher.

Doubleday and Company, Inc.: From the book *The Viruses* by Helena Curtis. Copyright © 1965 by Helena Curtis. From the book *How Old is the Earth?* by P. M. Hurley. Copyright © 1959 by Educational Services, Inc. Reprinted by permission of Doubleday and Company, Inc.

W. H. Freeman and Company: From *Principles of Geology,* Third Edition, by James Gilluly, Aaron C. Waters, and A. O. Woodford. W. H. Freeman and Company. Copyright © 1968.

Holt, Rinehart and Winston, Inc.: Reprinted from *Modern Earth Science* by W. L. Ramsey and R. A. Burckley. Copyright © 1965 by Holt, Rinehart and Winston, Inc. Used by permission of the publishers, Holt, Rinehart and Winston, Inc.

J. B. Lippincott Company: From *Science of Biology* by D. F. Miller and B. B. Vance, copyright 1965 by J. B. Lippincott. Reprinted by permission of the publishers.

Lyons and Carnahan: From *Chemistry and You,* by Baker, Bradbury, Eichinger, and Sigler. Copyright 1966 by Lyons and Carnahan, Educational Division, Meredith Corporation. Reprinted by permission of the publishers.

The Macmillan Company: Reprinted with permission of The Macmillan Company from pages 265 to 266 and 483 to 485 from *Physics: A Modern Approach* by L. Paul Elliot and William F. Wilcox. © 1957 by The Macmillan Company.

The New American Library, Inc.: From *The Oscillating Universe* by Ernst J. Opik, Copyright © 1960 by Ernst J. Opik. Published by arrangement with The New American Library, Inc., New York.

Prentice-Hall, Inc.: From L. Don Leet and Sheldon Judson, *Physical Geology,* Third Edition, © 1965, pp. 135–136. Reprinted by permission of Prentice-Hall, Inc., Englewood Cliffs, New Jersey.

W. B. Saunders Company: From *Basic Facts of General Chemistry,* by S. M. Brooks, copyright 1956. Reprinted by permission of the publishers.

Van Nostrand Reinhold Company: From *Physics: A Basic Science,* Third Edition, by Elmer E. Burns, Frank L. Verwiebe, Herbert C. Hazel and Gordon E. Van Hooft, Copyright 1943 (First Edition), 1948 (Second Edition), 1954 (Third Edition) by Litton Educational Publishing, Inc. From *Chemistry: A Basic Science* by John C. Hogg, Otis E. Alley and Charles L. Bickel, Copyright 1957 by Litton

CONTENTS

INTRODUCTION

The purpose of this book is to help you pass the "Reading Comprehension in the Natural Sciences" section of the High School Equivalency Examination. It contains instruction, drills, and tests covering everything you must know in order to pass the test. Later in this Introduction you will find a detailed description of how this book can help you, but first read the description of the actual test you will take.

THE TEST YOU WILL TAKE

The Science section of the High School Equivalency Examination measures your ability to read, understand, and interpret selections from written scientific material. The test can usually be completed in two hours. You may request a reasonable amount of additional time from the examiner, but it is not always practical for him to grant it.

Several different forms of the science test are now in use. An average test consists of ten passages, each 30 to 35 lines long, with a total of about 65 questions. You must read each selection and then answer from five to nine questions based on its content. The test usually contains five passages of material from the biological sciences and five from the fields of chemistry, physics, and earth science, which includes astronomy. Other forms of the "Reading Comprehension in the Natural Sciences" Test vary slightly.

The questions usually require the test-taker either to choose an answer that directly or indirectly repeats information given in the passage, or to infer an answer from the material he has just read or from this material plus a general knowledge of science. Every question has four possible answer choices, from which you must select the BEST answer. This means that for some questions, more than one correct answer is given, but one of these answers the question more fully or more precisely, and this is the BEST choice.

Each answer choice is numbered. On your answer sheet, you must blacken the space under the number of the correct answer. To understand the answering process more clearly, look at the following example.

DIRECTIONS: Read the following passage. Then answer the questions. Choose the BEST answer to each question. Then mark the space under that number in the answer column.

A seed, in order to release from its food supply the energy necessary for germination and early growth, requires oxygen so that the oxidation of food may take place. Hence, a constant supply of fresh air is an important factor in germination of a seed. It is necessary that air should penetrate between the grains of soil around the seed.

1. 1 2 3 4

1. A seed needs air so that
    (1)   it can grow.
    (2)   it may be kept cool.
    (3)   oxidation of its food supply may take place.
    (4)   none of the above

2. 1 2 3 4

2. One purpose of plowing a field before sowing seeds in it is to
    (1)   drain the soil.
    (2)   break up solidly packed soil so that air can penetrate to the seeds when they are sown.
    (3)   kill weeds before sowing seeds.
    (4)   all of the above

Answers and Explanations

1. **(3)** Although it is true that a seed needs air to grow, choice (1), the specific reason given in the passage for this need is that oxidation of the seed's food supply may take place. Thus, (3) is the BEST choice. There is nothing in the passage concerning temperature and growth of seeds. From your general knowledge, you know that cool weather holds back the growth of seeds. For these two reasons, you would not choose (2) as a correct choice. Since two of the answers are true and one of these is the correct choice, (4) cannot be correct.

2. **(2)** In considering choice (1), you reason that plowing the soil need not necessarily drain it, and not all soil needs draining, so (1) does not apply as a general rule. Thus, choice (1) cannot be correct. You learn from the passage that germinating seeds need air, so you can infer that choice (2) is the correct answer. Considering choice (3), you reason that, even if plowing kills some weeds, fresh weed seeds will have as much chance to grow as crop seeds. Hence, (3) is not a correct choice. Since two of the choices are not true, choice (4) cannot be correct.

	1	2	3	4		1	2	3	4		1	2	3	4
1.	‖	‖	■	‖	**6.**	‖	‖	‖	‖	**11.**	‖	‖	‖	‖
2.	‖	■	‖	‖	**7.**	‖	‖	‖	‖	**12.**	‖	‖	‖	‖
3.	‖	‖	‖	‖	**8.**	‖	‖	‖	‖	**13.**	‖	‖	‖	‖
4.	‖	‖	‖	‖	**9.**	‖	‖	‖	‖	**14.**	‖	‖	‖	‖
5.	‖	‖	‖	‖	**10.**	‖	‖	‖	‖	**15.**	‖	‖	‖	‖

An important note: Answer *all* questions, even if you have to guess. Some of your guesses are sure to be correct, and you will gain valuable points, which you would lose if you leave any questions unanswered.

HOW THIS BOOK WILL HELP YOU

This book has been designed to help you choose the *correct* answers. It contains instructional materials and exercises to aid you in answering questions based on word or passage meaning.

Remember that the "Interpretation of Reading Materials in the Natural Sciences" examination tests your reading ability as well as your knowledge of science. If you have trouble with reading comprehension, you are probably weak in one or more certain basic reading skills which everyone must master in order to read with understanding. This book explains what these skills are and shows you how you can develop them. As you study each skill, you will acquire a greater ability to read factual writing and knowledge about how scientific terms are used. This knowledge will help you to interpret what you read more accurately, and in greater depth.

The Reading Comprehension and Vocabulary Skills chapter also provides instruction on improving your vocabulary skills. You should study this material carefully and remember to put into practice all that you have learned every time you read. It is only by becoming aware of words, how they are put together, and how they are used that you can increase your vocabulary. The ability to handle words will be invaluable to you not only for passing the High School Equivalency Examination but also for any reading that you will do later on.

To find out how well you can read written scientific material now, take the Diagnostic Test. This test has been designed to point out your present strengths and weaknesses in reading and interpreting written scientific material, including diagrams, graphs, and charts. Study the instructional material in biology, chemistry, physics, and earth science. Then review the parts that gave you trouble. You should also study the GLOSSARY, which contains additional definitions and examples of terms you may be asked to identify on the High School Equivalency Examination. The Exercises will help you develop particular skills, and the Tests, which duplicate the kinds of questions that appear on the actual High School Equivalency Examination, will provide you with additional practice. Fully explained answers for all Exercises and Tests appear at the end of each chapter.

At the end of the book is a Simulated High School Equivalency Test in Interpretation of Reading Materials in the Natural Sciences. It contains 10 passages and 65 questions. The test reflects the format and kinds of questions asked on the actual High School Equivalency Examination. Take it after you have studied *all* of the material in this book. Allow yourself two hours to take the test, and then check your answers. If you did not do well, review the areas which gave you the most trouble.

TEST-TAKING TIPS

Read the following test-taking tips several times. Remembering and applying these suggestions will result in a higher score.

First, scan the questions to get an idea of the kind of information asked for; *second*, skim (read over quickly) the passage to get a general idea of the topic; *third*, close-read the passage (read the passage thoroughly and carefully, trying to extract all the meaning that the author put in); *fourth*, read each question carefully, then mark the best answer choice, going back to the passage when necessary.

DO answer each question on the basis of information contained in the passage *or* from your knowledge of science. DON'T answer on the basis of what you think the passage should say or the manner in which you would have asked the questions had you been the author of the test; answer in terms of what the *passage* states or implies.

DO notice whether a question refers to a specific line, sentence, or quotation from the passage. The answer, or the clue to the answer, to such a question is almost certain to be found in or near the line(s) referred to.

DO work as quickly as you can. This does not mean that you should be in such a hurry that you read the passages only superficially. It means, instead, that you should concentrate on what you are doing and work at a steady pace. Since your time is limited, don't waste precious minutes in worrying or daydreaming.

DO watch out for answers that seem too easy. If the words in a question and an answer choice are almost the same, that answer choice is not *necessarily* correct. Test-writers usually include some tricky questions.

DO choose the BEST answer (the most complete, accurate, or appropriate answer) to each question. Often, more than once choice *seems* correct. You must select the one which answers the question most precisely and completely.

DO answer easier questions first. If a passage or a question seems particularly difficult, jot down the passage or question number on a separate sheet of paper. After you have completed the rest of the test, go back and tackle the hard questions again.

DON'T expect the order of the questions to follow the order of the passage. Often, you must skip from one part of the passage to another in order to find an answer.

DON'T expect to find answers to all of the questions stated directly in the passage. Frequently, clues to the answer will be stated, and you will need to infer the correct answer on the basis of those clues. At other times, you will be asked to use your scientific knowledge and your reasoning power plus the material in the passage in order to reach a logical conclusion that is not in the passage at all.

DON'T look in just one sentence or paragraph for information unless you are sure that the correct answer is to be found in that particular part of the passage. Often, the thread of an answer winds through the whole reading selection.

DON'T leave any questions unanswered. On the High School Equivalency Examination, *blank answer spaces are marked wrong. Guess rather than leave an answer blank.*

THE DIAGNOSTIC TEST

The following Diagnostic Test has been carefully designed to measure your present level of ability to understand and interpret printed scientific material. The form of the Diagnostic Test closely resembles the form of the "Interpretation of Reading Materials in the Natural Sciences" section of the High School Equivalency Examination, except that: (1) it is only half as long; (2) you should complete it in half the time—one hour, instead of two hours; and (3) you will mark your answers in the spaces provided in the margin of each page instead of on a separate answer sheet.

Before you take this Diagnostic Test, be sure that you have the necessary supplies. You will need a clock or watch and several sharpened pencils. Find a quiet and comfortable place to work where you will not be interrupted.

A word of warning: the Diagnostic Test is *difficult*, as difficult as a real High School Equivalency Examination. On the actual test—and on this test as well—*you only have to answer half of the questions correctly in order to get a passing score*. But don't be satisfied with just a passing score; aim for a high score. If you do poorly on another part of the test, but achieve a high score on the science test, your overall average may be high enough for you to receive a diploma or certificate.

In any case, don't become nervous or upset if you can't understand all of the passages or answer all of the questions. Whatever you do, don't stop working before the hour is up because you feel that the test is too hard and you're not doing well. You may score higher than you expect. Furthermore, this book has been carefully designed to give you the kind of help you need. The less you know now, the more this book has to offer you—if you will study it patiently and thoroughly.

After you have taken the Diagnostic Test you will receive instructions on scoring it and on evaluating your present strengths and weaknesses in interpreting printed scientific material.

DIRECTIONS: Read each of the following passages. Choose the BEST answer to each question. Then blacken the space under that number in the answer column. You may go back to the passage as often as necessary to answer the questions.

ANSWERS AND EXPLANATIONS APPEAR AT THE END OF THE TEST

I

Matter in the gaseous state is characterized by its lack of any definite volume or shape. If a gas is placed in a closed container, it rapidly expands and very quickly becomes uniformly distributed throughout the entire space in the container. When a gas is cooled sufficiently, it becomes a liquid. Although all gases may be liquefied, some are changed to the liquid state only with a great deal of difficulty. Hydrogen and helium gases are the most difficult to liquefy, since temperatures near 0° A [absolute] are necessary. On the other hand, such gases as chlorine and ammonia are liquefied quite easily.

If two gases are placed in a container, each gas acts independently of the other and diffuses uniformly throughout the volume of the container.

Gases may undergo expansion and compression. Air forced into an automobile tire is compressed; when the air is allowed to escape, it expands. Gases also exert pressure, and this pressure is exerted uniformly on all sides and top and bottom of the containing vessel. It is a remarkable fact that the physical behavior of gases is to a large degree independent of their nature or composition; for example, all gases respond in the same manner to changes in temperature and pressure. Several so-called gas laws describe this physical behavior.

A mercury barometer

The pressure of the atmosphere is measured with an instrument called a *barometer*. A simple barometer can be prepared by inverting a piece of glass tubing about three feet long and closed at one end, filled with mercury, over a shallow pan containing mercury. The open end of the tube lies beneath the surface of the mercury in the pan. The mercury will sink in the tube to such a level that the weight of the column of mercury is just equal to the weight of a column of air of equal cross section above the surface of the mercury in the pan. This column of air extends many miles high. The air exerts a pressure on the surface of the mercury in the container and supports the column of mercury in the tube. The exact pressure is determined by reading the difference between two mercury levels, the one in the tube and the other in the pan. The height of the mercury column is usually expressed in terms of millimeters. The average air pressure at sea level will support a column of mercury 760 mm in height; this pressure is termed 1 atmosphere of pressure or *standard pressure*. A pressure of 50 atmospheres would be a pressure 50 times as great as that exerted by the atmosphere at sea level. In scientific work, pressures are usually referred to in terms of millimeters of mercury; thus a pressure of 700 mm would be a pressure equal to that exerted by a column of mercury 700 mm high. A column of water approximately 34 feet high would be supported by the atmosphere at sea level.

1. If you squeeze the gas from a round balloon into a sausage-shaped balloon, the gas will have
   (1) the shape of a sphere.   (3) the shape of a sausage.
   (2) no definite shape.   (4) none of the above

2. If two gases, such as hydrogen and helium, are placed in a container, each gas acts independently and
   (1) liquefies.   (3) diffuses uniformly.
   (2) undergoes compression.   (4) combines with the other.

3. Assuming that the moon has no atmosphere, a barometer on the moon's surface would read
   (1) 3 mm of mercury.   (3) 0.0 mm of mercury.
   (2) 0.5 mm of mercury.   (4) 760 mm of mercury.

4. Assume that the glass tube of a simple barometer must be at least three inches longer than the column of liquid it contains. The least length needed at sea level for a barometer using water as the liquid is
   (1) 35 feet.   (3) 34 feet.
   (2) $34\frac{1}{4}$ feet.   (4) 716 feet.

5. The gas trimethylamine is twice as heavy as air. If the earth's atmosphere consisted of trimethylamine, a mercury barometer at sea level would read
   (1) 876 mm.   (3) 380 mm.
   (2) 1520 mm.   (4) 760 mm.

6. If you have a volume of nitrogen and a volume of oxygen, the manner in which the two gases respond to changes in temperature and pressure will be
   (1) the same.
   (2) different.
   (3) the same for pressure but different for temperature.
   (4) the same for temperature but different for pressure.

II

Atoms and molecules of solids are organized in a regular array and are bound to each other by intermolecular forces of attraction. Although an atom or molecule of a solid may vibrate, it remains in a fixed position in relation to its neighbors. This ordered arrangement is upset by heat. When the temperature rises, the molecules remain closely attached, but in a less organized and regular array. The solid is then subject to alteration of its gross form and can be molded and bent.

As heat increases, the attractive forces become weaker, and the molecules no longer remain bound in a regular array. The solid melts, becoming a liquid. The point at which the solid melts depends on the strength of the intermolecular forces. The weaker the force, the lower the melting point.

If the intermolecular forces of a solid are very strong, as in most hard solids, a very high temperature is needed to break the bonds that maintain the orderly molecular pattern. If the intermolecular forces are weak, as in liquids at ordinary temperatures, the bonds may be broken at comparatively low temperatures.

When the temperature exceeds the melting point sufficiently, molecular motion becomes strong enough to completely counteract intermolecular forces. The molecules are pulled apart and fly off the surface of the liquid, and the substance boils. These molecules form a gas.

The normal sequence of transition from one state to another, as temperature increases, is solid to liquid, liquid to gas. However, there are certain substances that do not pass through the liquid state, but change directly from solid to gas. This direct transition is called *sublimation*. It may be easily observed when iodine crystals at room temperature change to a gas without passing through an intermediate liquid state. Ice is another example. Ice, of course, can be melted to water, but in cold climates one can observe snow—which is composed of ice crystals—disappearing during long periods of subfreezing weather. The snow has sublimated into the atmosphere without passing through the liquid state.

7. The changing of a solid directly to a gas is
   (1)   due to the strengthening of intermolecular forces by heat.
   (2)   due to the fact that gases have an orderly molecular pattern.
   (3)   an example of sublimation.
   (4)   none of the above

7. 1 2 3 4

8. A blacksmith uses fire to make a horseshoe because
   (1)   heat makes the molecular pattern of metals more orderly.
   (2)   horseshoes are usually made of iron.
   (3)   the regular pattern of a metal's atoms and molecules is less organized at high temperatures.
   (4)   fire may be controlled easily.

8. 1 2 3 4

9. 1 2 3 4

9. We say that iron is solid, water is liquid, and oxygen is gaseous, yet melted iron is liquid, water can be solid (ice) or gaseous (water vapor), and oxygen can be cooled to a liquid or solid. We decide whether to a call a substance a solid, liquid, or gas by
   (1) what the International Bureau of Weights and Measures says the substance is.
   (2) working out its molecular structure.
   (3) what the substance is at ordinary temperatures.
   (4) noting what state the substance is in between its melting and boiling points.

10. 1 2 3 4

10. On a windy day, when the temperature is below 32° F, clothes dry while hanging frozen on a clothesline. This is due to
    (1) the slower molecular motion of the ice in the clothes.
    (2) sublimation of the ice.
    (3) evaporation of water from the wet clothes.
    (4) both (1) and (2) of the above

11. 1 2 3 4

11. When sufficient heat is removed from a liquid, you should expect its molecules or atoms to
    (1) slow their motion.
    (2) form bonds.
    (3) arrange themselves in an orderly pattern.
    (4) all of the above

III

The ancient Greeks believed in an earth-centered, or geocentric, system of astronomy. Their belief in the geocentric system spread throughout the civilized world and became so entrenched in religion and in everyday life that it persisted for several centuries.

A few very enlightened individuals saw the obvious faults in the geocentric theory and proposed the heliocentric (sun-centered) system. Such men as Nicolaus Copernicus and Johannes Kepler, both of whom lived in the sixteenth century, produced careful scientific data to support their belief in the heliocentric theory.

Copernicus devised a heliocentric scheme of planetary motion and rotation of our solar system; a scheme that we know today to be true. He provided accurate calculations to prove that his theory was at least as plausible as any that had been conceived up to that time.

Kepler refined the Copernican heliocentric theory. Kepler's observations and calculations suggested that planets orbit in an eccentric elliptical path around the sun, and that the sun is not in the exact center of a planet's elliptical path.

His calculations showed that a planet traveling around the sun moves faster as its path comes closer to the sun. In other words, the closer the path of the planet is to the sun, the faster the planet travels.

Galileo Galilei, who lived from 1564 until 1642, produced the first convincing arguments for the heliocentric theory—arguments that were eventually to lead men to discard the geocentric theory. Galileo made three specific contributions:

1. He was the first to use a telescope scientifically for astronomical observations.
2. With his telescope, he observed phenomena that supported the heliocentric theory—phenomena that had not been observed before.
3. He gave vigorous support to the Copernican heliocentric theory.

Some of the things that Galileo observed were dark spots on the sun, the phases of the planet Venus, and the irregularities in the moon's surface.

For his part in enlightening mankind about the universe around him, Galileo was scorned by other scientists of his day. Galileo, who at one time was a prominent man in the church, was officially criticized by the church for belief in a doctrine thought to oppose the spiritual nature of man. It was the church's doctrine that the earth is the center of the universe, because God gave the earth to man.

Galileo and other scientists who courageously held to their beliefs in scientific truth were eventually to convince later generations of the true state of the solar system and of the merits of honest observation rather than prejudiced fallacy.

12. 1 2 3 4

12. The earth travels in its orbit
    (1) at an unvarying speed.
    (2) faster when it is closer to the sun.
    (3) faster when it is farther from the sun.
    (4) slower when it is closer to the sun.

13. 1 2 3 4

13. Nicolaus Copernicus argued that
    (1) the planets orbit around the sun.
    (2) the earth is an astronomical body with no orbital path but with axial rotation.
    (3) Jupiter orbits in an elliptical path.
    (4) the moon has several phases.

14. 1 2 3 4

14. Kepler's discoveries
    (1) took place before those of Copernicus.
    (2) took place after those of Copernicus.
    (3) were influenced by those of Copernicus.
    (4) both (2) and (3) of the above

15. 1 2 3 4

15. Galileo
    (1) made his discovery of dark spots on the sun with the same telescope that was used by Copernicus.
    (2) worked out the first sound proofs for the geocentric theory of the solar system.
    (3) discovered the phases of the moon.
    (4) none of the above

16. 1 2 3 4

16. Galileo's support of the Copernican heliocentric theory was
    (1) accepted by other scientists of his day.
    (2) criticized by the church.
    (3) later proved to be worthless.
    (4) not an influence upon his successors.

17. 1 2 3 4

17. Galileo's work was necessary for the establishment of the heliocentric theory because
    (1) Copernicus was unable to produce mathematical proof of his theory.
    (2) Kepler's conclusions were based on accurate observations, but lacked mathematical support.
    (3) Galileo was the first to provide mathematical proofs to corroborate the observations of his brilliant predecessors, Copernicus and Kepler.
    (4) none of the above

IV

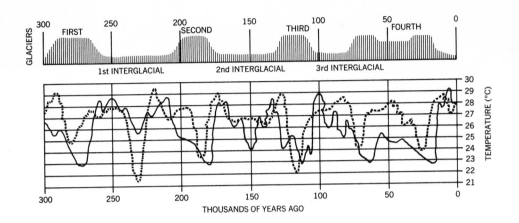

On the graph, the solid line represents ocean temperatures and the dotted line represents the amount of heat received from the sun during the last 300,000 years. The relationship between the temperatures and the last worldwide glaciers is shown above.

18. The amount of heat received from the sun during the past 300,000 years was at its lowest
    (1) 150,000 years ago.
    (2) about 130,000 years ago.
    (3) about 230,000 years ago.
    (4) about 30,000 years ago.

18. 1 2 3 4

19. The graph shows that, in general,
    (1) when less heat was received from the sun, the ocean temperature was low.
    (2) when less heat was received from the sun, the ocean temperature was higher.
    (3) there is no connection between ocean temperature and the amount of heat received from the sun.
    (4) none of the above

19. 1 2 3 4

20. The diagram shows
    (1) a perfect connection between the amount of heat received from the sun and the existence of glaciers.
    (2) that whenever there was a low point in the amount of heat received from the sun, a glacier existed.
    (3) that a low point in the amount of heat received from the sun did not always coincide with the existence of a glacier.
    (4) all of the above

20. 1 2 3 4

21. In general, the graph shows that changes in ocean temperature
    (1) coincide perfectly with the amount of heat from the sun.
    (2) lag several thousand years behind changes in the amount of heat received from the sun.
    (3) take place several thousand years before changes in the amount of heat received from the sun.
    (4) none of the above

21. 1 2 3 4

22.

1	2	3	4
‖	‖	‖	‖

22. Calling on your general knowledge and powers of reasoning, you would say that the amount of sea water being heated by the sun during a glacial period is
   (1) more than during an interglacial period.
   (2) less than during an interglacial period.
   (3) the same as during an interglacial period.
   (4) No answer can be given to this question.

V

In 1931, William J. Elford of the National Institute for Medical Research in England succeeded in developing a series of extremely fine graded filters. He was thus able to show that a virus could go through one filter but would be caught in another. From 1931 to 1935, Elford and his group studied most of the viruses for which animal hosts were available and showed that each type had a characteristic size, which actually he was able to estimate with remarkable accuracy. Now, although viruses had not been seen, it was known once and for all that they were particulate in nature, not a living fluid, and that, like other organisms, they have their own specific sizes and probably their own shapes also. So the viruses at last assumed a comfortable and respectable status, differing from the bacteria in certain regards, but in no way challenging man to seek new definitions of "life" or to make room for exceptions within the old. . . .

In one of those extraordinary flashes of illogical inspiration that contribute as much to science as the slow patient accumulation of knowledge one hears so much about, Wendell Stanley, a young biochemist at the Princeton laboratory of The Rockefeller Institute, set out to characterize a virus chemically. He chose tobacco mosaic, the virus of Beijerinck, because it was stable under a variety of conditions and safe to work with, and because the characteristic infection could be demonstrated easily and rapidly. In 1935, from the juice squeezed from a ton of tobacco leaves, Stanley was able to extract the first sample of pure virus. Then he showed that if this virus were isolated under certain conditions, it formed readily visible needle-like crystals. It could be kept in this form indefinitely. The virus was not a small bacterium. It was a molecule, a pure crystalline substance.

But when these crystals were put back into solution, they once more became infective, acquiring the classic properties of activity, hereditary continuity, and self-replication; in other words, these shimmering needles, these inert molecules, became alive, just like the lady's hair dropped in the rain barrel. As [Thomas Rivers, dean of American virologists,] said, the virus was either "organule" or "molechism," with the line of demarcation between the living and the nonliving too fine to be drawn.

23. Viruses were first shown to be particles and not a living fluid when they   **23.** 1 2 3 4
     (1)   were seen under an ultramicroscope.
     (2)   could be formed into crystals.
     (3)   could pass through one filter but be caught in a finer one.
     (4)   could be counted individually.

24. Viruses are said to be on the borderline between living and nonliving things   **24.** 1 2 3 4
     because

(1)   active infective viruses that reproduce themselves can be made into nonliving crystals.
(2)   viruses in crystalline form can be kept indefinitely.
(3)   the crystalline virus substance, put back into solution, becomes active infective particles that can reproduce themselves.
(4)   all of the above

25.   1   2   3   4

25.   In his famous experiment, Dr. Wendell Stanley found that nonliving virus crystals
(1)   can cause a characteristic infection.
(2)   are needle-like in shape.
(3)   reproduce themselves.
(4)   have offspring that are replicas of their parents.

26.   1   2   3   4

26.   Dr. Stanley chose the tobacco mosaic virus to use in demonstrating the chemical nature of viruses because this virus
(1)   was safe to work with.
(2)   caused a characteristic infection that could be easily and rapidly demonstrated.
(3)   was stable under a number of different conditions.
(4)   all of the above

27.   1   2   3   4

27.   It is possible for astronauts to bring back from the moon a virus that never before existed on earth because
(1)   the dusty, waterless surface of the moon is a good place for viruses to live.
(2)   without an atmosphere, the moon's surface receives more sunlight.
(3)   in crystalline form, a virus should exist indefinitely, even in the harsh conditions on the moon.
(4)   all of the above

28.   1   2   3   4

28.   When Dr. Rivers said a virus was either "organule" or "molechism," he was referring to the fact that
(1)   a virus seems to be both a living and a nonliving thing.
(2)   viruses seem to be particles and living fluids.
(3)   viruses seem to be a kind of bacteria.
(4)   all viruses are nonliving molecules.

ANSWERS AND EXPLANATIONS FOR THE DIAGNOSTIC TEST

1. **(3)** The first paragraph of the passage says that a gas becomes uniformly distributed throughout the entire space within its container. Thus, the gas would have the shape of a sausage, and (3) is the correct answer. (1), (2), and (4) are incorrect.

2. **(3)** The second paragraph of the passage beginning on page 6 states that if two gases are placed in a container, each gas acts independently of the other and diffuses uniformly throughout the volume of the container. (1) This could not be the correct answer because a gas must be cooled in order to liquefy it, and nothing is said in the question about cooling hydrogen and helium. (2) could not be correct as the volume of the container does not change. To compress a gas within a container, the volume must be reduced so that the gases are squeezed into a smaller space. (3) is the correct answer. (4) is not a logical answer. Nothing is said in the passage about the combining of gases.

3. **(3)** If the moon has no atmosphere at all, no weight will press down on the mercury in the pan and none will rise in the tube. Thus, the barometer will read 0.0. The correct choice, then, is (3).

4. **(2)** The passage states that the atmosphere at sea level supports a column of water 34 feet high. So the glass tube cannot be less than 34 feet long. But the question says that the tube must be 3 inches longer than the column of liquid; thus, 34 feet 3 inches, or $34\frac{1}{4}$ feet, of glass tube are needed. Hence, (2) is the correct answer.

5. **(2)** The fourth paragraph explains that the column of mercury is pushed up into the glass tube to a level at which the weight of the column of mercury equals the weight of a column of air of equal cross section. For air, the height of the mercury column is 760 millimeters. For trimethylamine, which weighs twice as much as air, a column of mercury 2×760 millimeters, or 1520 millimeters, would be necessary to equal the weight of a column of atmosphere of equal cross section. Thus, (2) is the correct answer.

6. **(1)** Paragraph three of the passage states that "all gases respond in the same manner to changes in temperature and pressure." Thus, (1) is the correct answer, and the other answers are logically eliminated.

7. **(3)** In the next-to-the-last paragraph, the changing of a solid directly to a gas is defined as sublimation. Thus, (3) is the correct choice. Paragraphs two and four state that, as heat increases, intermolecular forces are weakened and then completely counteracted. This is the opposite of what is stated in (1), making (1) incorrect. Paragraphs one, two, and four explain that heat destroys the orderly patterns of atoms and molecules in solids, changing the solids to liquids; and that a high degree of heat completely counteracts intermolecular forces, causing

molecules to fly off the surface of the liquid as it changes to a gas. From these facts, we can conclude that a gas does not have an orderly arrangement of molecules. Hence, (2) is not correct.

8. **(3)** The first paragraph states that the ordered arrangement of molecules and atoms of a solid is upset by heat and as a result the solid can be molded or bent. Thus, (3) is the correct answer, and (1) must be incorrect. It is true that horseshoes usually are made of iron (2) and that fire may be easily controlled (4), but neither of these facts provides a direct answer to the question.

9. **(3)** We call a substance solid, liquid, or gaseous by noting what it is at ordinary temperatures, since we usually deal with substances at ordinary temperatures. Thus, (3) is the correct answer. (*Note:* An Eskimo might say that water is solid.) The state—solid, liquid, or gaseous—of a substance is neither a weight nor a measure, so the International Bureau of Weights and Measures would not be concerned. Hence, (1) is incorrect. Although working out the molecular structure of a substance would tell us whether it is a solid, liquid, or gas, it would not tell us which structure to choose as the representative state of the substance. Thus, (2) is not correct. Paragraph four says that when the melting point of a substance is exceeded greatly enough, the substance boils. Thus, between melting and boiling points a substance is a liquid. Hence, (4) is incorrect.

10. **(2)** The last paragraph of the passage describes the sublimation of snow at subfreezing temperatures. Since snow is made up of ice crystals, and the question states the temperature is below freezing (32° F), we can reason that the clothes dry because the water on them freezes and then sublimates. Thus, (2) is the correct answer. Choice (1) cannot be correct because "the slower molecular motion of the ice" is a vague phrase that has no definite meaning. And (3) cannot be correct because, at temperatures below 32° F there would not be any water on the clothes; the water would be ice. Since (2) is the correct answer but (1) is incorrect, (4) must be incorrect.

11. **(4)** Basing your thinking on what happens to a solid when heated, it is reasonable to expect the reverse series of events when a liquid is cooled. Paragraphs one and three of the passage describe the increase in motion, the breaking of bonds, and the destruction of the orderly pattern of atoms or molecules as heat increases and a solid becomes a liquid. The reverse of this series of events is given in choices (1), (2), and (3); thus (4) is the correct answer.

12. **(2)** The fifth paragraph says that Kepler discovered that a planet moves faster as its path comes closer to the sun. Thus, (2) is the correct answer, and the other choices must be wrong since they contradict (2).

13. **(1)** Copernicus discovered the heliocentric nature of the solar system; thus, (1) is the correct answer. Since the earth does move around the sun in an orbit, (2) must be wrong. Choice (3) is a true statement, but was part of Kepler's, not Copernicus', discoveries. Choice (4) also is

a true statement, but is not connected to Copernicus either in the passage or in fact.

14. **(4)** Since Kepler worked out laws describing how the planets move in their orbits around the sun, he had to know that the sun was the center of the solar system; thus, his work had to follow and be influenced by the discoveries of Copernicus. Hence, (2) and (3) are true, and (4) is the correct answer. The fact that (2) and (3) are correct statements logically makes (1) incorrect.

15. **(4)** Galileo, the passage states, was the first to use the telescope for astronomical observations; thus, he could not have borrowed one used by Copernicus for the same purpose. The passage states that Galileo was a champion of the heliocentric, not the geocentric, theory of the solar system. Thus, (2) is incorrect. The passage states that Galileo discovered the phases of Venus, not of the moon (3). All of the choices being wrong, (4) is the correct answer.

16. **(2)** The next-to-the-last paragraph states that Galileo was criticized by the church for his belief that the earth is not the center of the universe. Hence, (2) is the correct answer. The next-to-the-last paragraph also states that Galileo was scorned by other scientists of his day for his support of the heliocentric theory. Thus (1) is not correct. The last paragraph says that Galileo's work convinced later generations of the true state of the solar system. Thus, (3) and (4) are not correct.

17. **(4)** The passage specifically notes the mathematical proofs given by both Copernicus and Kepler for their astronomical theories. Hence, (1) and (2) are not true. According to the passage, Galileo backed the theories of Copernicus and Kepler by his observations with a telescope, not with mathematical proofs. Thus, (3) is not true. With (1), (2), and (3) not true, (4) is the correct answer.

18. **(3)** The dotted line dips to its lowest point approximately 230,000 years ago. Thus, (3) is the correct answer.

19. **(1)** In general, the line representing ocean temperature is low when the line representing heat received from the sun is low. Thus, (1) is the correct answer. One of the answers being correct, the others must, logically, be incorrect.

20. **(3)** Although all the glacial periods coincide with low points, the lowest point on the curve representing the amount of heat received from the sun (about 230,000 years ago) coincides with an interglacial period. Therefore, (3) is the correct answer. Choices (1) and (2), which both say practically the same thing in different words, contradict (3) and are both incorrect.

21. **(2)** The changes in the solid line lag behind those in the dotted line, thus showing that changes in ocean temperature lagged behind those changes in heat received from the sun. Hence, (2) is the correct answer. With (2) being correct, the other choices are excluded logically.

22. **(2)** During a glacial period there is an extraordinarily large amount of ice on the earth's surface. This ice comes from snow which formed from water vapor in the atmosphere. The water vapor in the atmosphere is replenished by water from the oceans. Thus, there is less water in the oceans to be heated by the sun during a glacial period.

23. **(3)** The first paragraph of the passage describes how one investigator showed that viruses could pass through one filter and be caught in a finer filter, thus proving that a virus is a kind of particle. Hence, (3) is the correct answer. The passage states directly that at the time viruses were proved to be particles, they had not been seen. Thus, (1) is wrong. Although the passage says that crystals were formed from viruses, it makes no connection between this fact and the identification of viruses as particles; hence, (2) is not correct. Nothing is said in the passage, and no conclusion can be drawn from the passage, concerning the counting of viruses as a means of identification. Hence, (4) is incorrect.

24. **(4)** The last two paragraphs describe the chain of events contained in answers (1), (2), and (3). Thus, all are true statements and (4) is the correct answer.

25. **(2)** The third paragraph states that the crystals of the tobacco mosaic virus are needle-like in shape. Thus, (2) is the correct answer. The third paragraph lists all the characteristics stated in answers (1), (3), and (4), saying that they are exhibited by living viruses that result from virus crystals being put back in solution, not by a nonliving crystalline virus substance. Thus, all of these answers are wrong.

26. **(4)** The second paragraph says that Stanley chose the tobacco mosaic virus for all of the reasons given in (1), (2), and (3); thus, (4) is the correct answer.

27. **(3)** The passage states directly that virus substance in crystalline form can exist indefinitely. This substance, being nonliving, could survive the harsh conditions on the moon. Thus, (3) is the correct answer. The passage explains that viruses are alive when they are in solution; thus, the dry surface of the moon would not provide any liquid in which live viruses could be in solution. Thus, (1) cannot be a correct choice. The second statement does not make it clear that the moon's surface receives more sunlight; furthermore, no connection between viruses and sunlight is made in the passage. Hence, (2) is incorrect.

28. **(1)** Inspection of the terms "molechism" and "organule" reveals that they are made up thus: *molec*(ule) + (organ)*ism;* and *organ*(ism) + (molec)*ule*. Further, Rivers' comment is found in the part of the passage (the end of paragraph two and most of paragraph three) which discusses the fact that viruses may be molecules or living substances (organisms). Thus, (1) is the correct answer. Paragraph one explains that Elford's filtration experiments proved that viruses *are* particles and *are not* living fluid. Hence, (2) is incorrect. The next-to-

the-last sentence of paragraph two states that Stanley's experiment proved that a virus is not a bacterium. Thus, (3) is not correct. The material in paragraphs two and three explains that a virus may be a nonliving molecule; it also may be a living organism. Hence, *all* viruses are not nonliving molecules, and (3) is incorrect.

NOW TURN THE PAGE FOR INSTRUCTIONS ON MARKING YOUR SELF-EVALUATION PROFILE.

SELF-EVALUATION PROFILE

1. Go back to question 1 of the Diagnostic Test. Notice that the number 1 appears in Category III of the Self-Evaluation Profile below. If you answered question 1 correctly, circle the number 1 in the Category III column. Continue to do this for all your answers. CIRCLE ONLY YOUR CORRECT ANSWERS ON THE CHART.

2. After you have circled each correct answer in the appropriate column, add up the number of right answers in each category and place the totals in the NUMBER RIGHT column.

3. Compare these scores with the numbers in the QUESTION TOTAL column. This will give you an indication of which areas you should study the most.

	Question Total	Number Right
Category I **BIOLOGY** 23, 24, 25, 26, 27, 28	6	
Category II **CHEMISTRY** 7, 8, 9, 10, 11	5	
Category III **PHYSICS** 1, 2, 3, 4, 5, 6	6	
Category IV **EARTH SCIENCE** (including astronomy) 12, 13, 14, 15, 16, 17, 18, 19, 20, 21, 22	11	
TOTAL	28	

It is impossible to predict with statistical accuracy how well you would do on an actual High School Equivalency Examination. You will be given any one of several current forms of the test, some of which will seem harder to one individual than to another. Therefore, *consider the Self-Evaluation Profile as a guide, not a guarantee. And remember,* if you study the material in this book carefully, your score is bound to improve.

READING COMPREHENSION AND VOCABULARY SKILLS

The science section of the GED Examination tests your ability to comprehend facts, ideas, and relationships contained in a number of reading passages. The questions following these selections ask you to think about the passages in ways that may be unfamiliar to you. Such thinking often requires learning and practicing new reading skills. This chapter will help you to think about passages in new ways. It will also help you answer GED Test questions. Only by answering the questions correctly can you show that you have understood what you have read.

Written science material is descriptive. It details the steps or parts of a process in nature or in man's scientific or engineering activities. For example, scientific passages may describe how a plant reproduces, from the sprouting of a seed to the growth of the plant, flowering of the plant, fertilization of the flowers, production of new seeds, and dispersal of the seeds. Or, scientific passages may tell you how to proceed with an experiment to prove that water at 4° C is heavier than ice at 0° C. Or, they may detail the process for getting sulfur out of the ground.

Written science material is explanatory. Insofar as is possible, science is interested in explaining how and why things happen in nature and in man-made processes. For example, a physicist or engineer may explain how and why a rocket works. Or, a chemist might explain how aluminum is obtained from aluminum ore and why the process that is used works.

Usually, the descriptive and explanatory parts of scientific writing are combined. In order to explain how a diesel engine works, it is necessary to describe the parts of the engine and their location. Or, to explain how a glacier acts, it is necessary to describe the parts and movements of the glacier.

From the foregoing, you can see that written material in the sciences is *factual* and *detailed*. When reading passages of science material, you must pay careful attention to detail. The scientist is not interested, as are writers in other fields, in arousing emotions, setting moods, or using words in pleasing or striking patterns. Although you, as an individual, may have an emotional response to reading certain scientific writings, it was not the object of the author to arouse that feeling. Thus, when you read science, you may ignore all but facts, ideas, and the relationships between them.

In most questions you will be asked about the scientific material you have read, the answer will be found in one or more facts. You will probably never be asked to tell what the general or overall thought of the passage is. However, you may be asked a specific question that will make it necessary for you to know the general idea of a part of, or the whole of, a passage.

DIRECTIONS: What is the general, main, or overall idea of each of the following passages? Check your answers against the correct answers at the end of the exercise.

1. First, the ground is raked level, then fertilizer and grass seed are put down. Later, lime is spread on the raked and fertilized ground. Finally, the ground is thoroughly sprinkled with water.

2. Ancient man believed the basic elements to be fire, earth, water, and air. Medieval alchemists (the forerunners of modern chemists) recognized that matter consists of many more basic units than the four elements of the ancients. In the eighteenth century, John Dalton made significant observations about the basic unit of matter, the atom. Throughout the nineteenth century, the atom was considered to be a hard, round, indivisible particle. Toward the beginning of the twentieth century, scientific investigation began to suggest that the atom could be divided into smaller particles.

3. The most important concept in all nature is energy. It represents a fundamental entity common to all forms of matter in all parts of the physical world. Closely associated with energy is work. To a layman, *work* is a word used to describe the expenditure of one's physical or mental energy. In science, work is a quantity that is the product of force times the distance through which the force acts. In other words, work is done when force moves an object. Work and energy are related because energy is the ability to do work.

ANSWERS

1. Planting grass seed involves several definite steps or operations.

2. The concept of nature as composed of many separate units is not new to modern man, but has been developing since ancient times.

3. The most important concept in nature is energy, which is common to all parts of the physical world and is closely related to energy.

DIRECTIONS: Using again the passages from which we have just noted the main ideas, we will now see how specific questions might be asked about the same subject matter. In these questions, choose the correct answer from those offered. Check your answers against the correct answers at the end of the exercise.

1. First, the ground is raked level, then fertilizer and grass seed are put down. Later, lime is spread on the raked and fertilized ground. Finally, the ground is thoroughly sprinkled with water.

After lime is spread on the ground, it is
(1) raked level.
(3) watered.
(2) sown with grass seed.
(4) fertilized.

2. Ancient man believed the basic elements to be fire, earth, water, and air. Medieval alchemists (the forerunners of modern chemists) recognized that matter consists of many more basic units than the four elements of the ancients. In the eighteenth century, John Dalton made significant observations about the basic unit of matter, the atom. Throughout the nineteenth century, the atom was considered to be a hard, round, indivisible particle. Toward the beginning of the twentieth century, scientific investigation suggested that the atom could be divided into smaller particles.

Medieval alchemists believed matter to be made up of
(1) fire, earth, water, and air.
(3) hard, round, indivisible particles.
(2) atoms.
(4) none of the above

3. The most important concept in all nature is energy. It represents a fundamental entity common to all forms of matter in all parts of the physical world. Closely associated with energy is work. To a layman, *work* is a word used to describe the expenditure of one's physical and mental energy. In science, work is a quantity that is the product of force times the distance through which the force acts. In other words, work is done when force moves an object. Work and energy are related because energy is the ability to do work.

If a man pushes hard and long against the side of a large building, the man is
(1) doing much work.
(2) not doing any work.
(3) doing some work.
(4) both (2) and (3) of the above

ANSWERS

1. A careful reading of the passage shows that the order of operations is (a) raking level, (b) putting down fertilizer and grass seed, (c) spreading lime, and (d) sprinkling with water. With these four facts in mind, you can see that (3) is the correct answer.

2. Upon reading the passage, we find in the second sentence a direct statement that medieval alchemists recognized that matter consists of many more basic units than the basic four of the ancients. This factual statement eliminates (1) as a possible correct answer. Further reading of the passage reveals no connection between the alchemists and atoms or the idea that atoms were hard, round, indivisible particles. Therefore, neither (2) nor (3) could be a correct choice. Since neither (1), (2), nor (3) is correct, (4) is a true statement and is the correct answer to the question.

3. A rereading of the passage reveals that the answer cannot be found directly in the passage. The answer must be obtained by reasoning. We find in the passage that work is done when force moves an object. The man, of course, does not move the building by pushing against it. Thus, he is not

doing any work. Therefore (1), (3) and (4) must be incorrect. This is the same statement we find in (2); hence, (2) is a correct answer. Although the man cannot move the building, his effort undoubtedly could move a lighter object, such as a wheelbarrow. By moving the wheelbarrow, he would be doing work. Work is the product of force times the distance through which the force acts ($W = F \times D$).

UNDERSTANDING DIAGRAMS, CHARTS, AND GRAPHS

Diagrams, charts, and graphs are graphic representations of facts. They are often used to help explain a reading passage on the Natural Sciences section of the GED Test.

A *diagram* is a picture that explains something by showing its workings or parts.

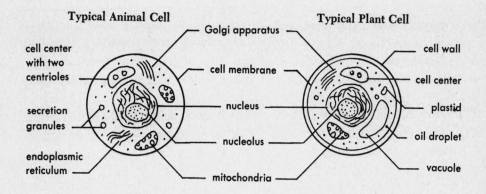

A *chart* is a table, picture, or other graphic representation used to explain and clarify facts.

Percentages of different grain size fractions of lower Mississippi River sediments, 100 to 1000 miles (160 to 1660 kilometers) below Cairo, Ill.

	Miles below Cairo, Illinois					
Grain size	*100*	*300*	*500*	*700*	*900*	*1000*
Gravel	29	8	14	5	trace	none
Coarse sand	30	22	9	8	1	none
Medium sand	32	50	46	44	26	9
Fine sand	8	19	28	41	70	69
Silt	trace	trace	2	1	2	10
Clay	trace	trace	1	trace	1	10

SOURCE: After Charles M. Nevin; from data of the U.S. Waterways Experiment Station, Vicksburg, Mississippi.

A *graph* is a representation by lines or bars of changes in one quantity in relation to another. The graph usually includes a grid of lines that indicate amounts of the two varying quantities.

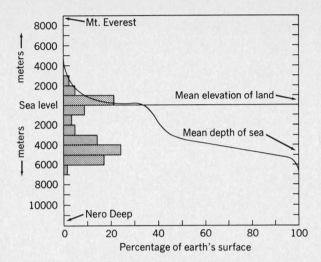

Graph showing percentages of the earth's surface lying between various levels above and below the sea. The bars at left represent percentages (scale below) lying between the respective levels, at intervals of 1000 meters. Note the two broad flat areas in the curve, one near sea level, the other 4,000 to 5,000 meters below sea level.

On the examination, you will be given passages and questions that refer to diagrams, charts, and graphs. Here is an example.

Passage: Loudness is due to amplitude. In the diagram below, the amplitude is the distance of the crest or the trough of a wave from its midline. As the amplitude of the wave becomes less as it moves away from the source of the sound, so the loudness decreases as you move away from the source. When sounds are made louder, as in a radio amplifier, the wave amplitude is increased. This is done by using a greater amount of energy to produce the sound vibrations.

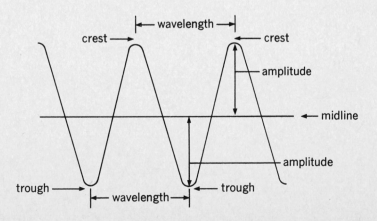

The number of times an object vibrates per second is its frequency of vibration. The frequency of vibration determines the pitch of a sound. If you strike a C tuning fork, its prongs will vibrate 256 times a second. No matter how hard you hit the fork, it will still vibrate 256 times a second.

Question: If the amplitude of the wave in the diagram became greater, the sound it represents would become

(1) less.   (3) higher.
(2) louder.   (4) lower.

Answer: The correct answer is (2), the sound would become louder.

When answering questions involving diagrams, refer to the reading passage as often as necessary in order to understand the diagram. Although the diagram explains an idea in the passage, you must read the passage in order to understand the diagram well enough to answer the questions.

VOCABULARY SKILLS

The vocabulary section of this book has been designed to help you prepare for the science section of the GED Test. Here you will study the basic parts of words—prefixes, roots, and suffixes. A knowledge of these commonly used word parts will enable you to figure out the meanings of many unfamiliar words.

English words are constructed of word parts, called *prefixes, roots,* and *suffixes.* Different combinations of these word parts produce different words. The *root* is the basic part of any word, the part that gives the word its essential meaning. The essential meaning may be altered or changed completely by adding another word part to the beginning or the end of the root. The word part that is attached to the beginning of the root is a *prefix.* The word part that is attached at the end of the root is a *suffix.* By knowing the meanings of these basic word parts that appear over and over again in different English words, you will be able to make a good guess as to the meanings of many words that are now totally unfamiliar to you. To get an idea of how this system of word construction works, study the following lists.

PREFIXES

Prefix	Meaning	Example	Meaning
1. **ante**	before	antenatal	occurring before birth
2. **anti**	(1) against (2) opposed to	(1) anticoagulant (2) antibody	(1) a substance that acts against the coagulation (clotting) of blood (2) a chemical substance with which the body opposes the toxins of harmful bacteria
3. **bi**	two	bivalve	an animal with a two-valved shell, such as an oyster
4. **circum**	around	circumscribe	to draw a line around
5. **contra**	against	contraception	the prevention of conception
6. **de**	from, down, away	(1) decolor (2) deposition (3) dehydrate	(1) to remove color from (2) to lay down (3) to take water away
7. **fore**	before, in front of	(1) forecast (2) forebrain	(1) a prediction of a future event or condition, such as the weather (2) the front division of the developing brain of mammals
8. **im, in, ir**	not	(1) immature (2) inaudible (3) irregular	(1) not mature (2) not capable of being heard (3) not regular
9. **per**	(1) by means of (2) through (3) thoroughly	(1) percent (2) percolate (3) perchlorinated	(1) by means of a hundred (2) to ooze or drip through (3) chlorinated thoroughly
10. **post**	after	postnatal	after birth
11. **trans**	(1) across (2) beyond	(1) transatlantic (2) transuranic	(1) across the Atlantic Ocean (2) beyond uranium in atomic weight

ROOTS

Root	Meaning	Examples	Meaning
1. **chrome**	colored, colored matter	(1) chromatic (2) achromatic (3) polychrome	(1) highly colored (2) possessing no hue (3) having or made in several colors

Root	Meaning	Examples	Meaning
2. cur, cour	to run	(1) current (2) courier (3) course	(1) running (or flowing) matter, such as water or electricity (2) a person who runs for a purpose, such as to deliver something (3) to run dogs or birds in a race
3. duce, duct	lead	(1) induce (2) conductor (3) ductless	(1) to lead one to do (2) one who leads (3) without ducts, tubes, or channels
4. fact, fect	to make, to cause	(1) manufacture (2) artifact (3) infect	(1) to make by hand or by machine (2) an object made by human art or skill (3) to cause to be contaminated by bacteria or viruses
5. gen, geno, gene	birth, race, kind	(1) genetics (2) congenital (3) gene	(1) science of heredity, including birth characteristics and variations (2) existing at or from birth (3) an element of germ plasm that transmits hereditary characteristics
6. hydr, hydro	water	(1) hydrology (2) hydrate (3) dehydrate	(1) the study of the actions of water on the land (2) to combine with water (3) to remove water from
7. logy	study of, science of	(1) geology (2) biological (3) logistic	(1) science of the study of the earth, and rocks in particular (2) pertaining to the science of living things (biology) (3) of or relating to the study of symbolic logic
8. meter	measure	(1) metric (2) thermometer (3) metronome	(1) a system of measurement based on the meter as a standard of length (2) an instrument for measuring temperature (3) an instrument designed to mark (measure) exact intervals of time by repeated clicks

Root	Meaning	Examples	Meaning
9. phon, phono	sound, speech, voice	(1) telephone (2) phonic (3) phonetic	(1) an instrument for conveying sound over a distance (2) pertaining to, or producing, sound (3) of or relating to the voice and speech
10. scope	to see	(1) telescope (2) iconoscope (3) microscopic	(1) an instrument for seeing objects at a distance (2) a device in a television camera for producing visual electronic images (3) invisible without the use of a microscope
11. sec	cut	(1) dissect (2) trisect (3) section	(1) to cut or separate into pieces or parts (2) to cut or divide into three parts (3) to cut across
12. struc	to build	(1) construct (2) destruction (3) structure	(1) to put together, make, or build (2) the action or process of destroying something (3) a building or other built object
13. tact	touch	(1) tactile (2) intact (3) contact	(1) perceptible by touch (2) untouched, especially by anything that harms or lessens (3) to be touching or in touch with; the state of touching
14. tele	far, at a distance	(1) telegraph (2) television (3) telephotography	(1) an instrument for sending messages over distances by means of coded electrical signals (2) an electronic system for sending and receiving pictures at a distance (3) photography at a distance, especially with a lens that provides a large image
15. tend, tens	stretch	(1) tendon (2) tension (3) intense	(1) stretchable fibrous connective tissue by which muscles are attached to bones (2) the act of stretching or the condition or degree of being stretched taut (3) strained or stretched or straining to the utmost

SUFFIXES

Suffix	Meaning	Example	Meaning
1. **able, ible**	capable of being	filterable	capable of being filtered
2. **ance**	amount or degree	conductance	degree to which a conductor transmits electric current
3. **al**	of or characterized by	electrical	of or characterized by electricity
4. **ible** (*see* **able**)	capable of being	divisible	capable of being divided
5. **ic**	pertaining to or like	cosmic	pertaining to, or like, the cosmos (the universe as a whole)
6. **ion**	(1) act or process (2) state or condition	(1) hydration (2) calcification	(1) the act or process of combining with water (2) the state of having deposits of calcium
7. **ist**	one who specializes in a specific science or skill	chemist	a person who specializes in the science of chemistry
8. **itis**	disease, irritation, or inflammation of	appendicitis	inflammation or disease of the appendix
9. **ity**	quality, state, or degree	alkalinity	quality, state, or degree of being alkaline
10. **ive**	performing or tending toward an indicated action	nutritive	providing or tending to provide nutrition (nourishment)
11. **ize**	to make or become like	crystallize	to make or become a crystal
12. **oid**	resembling a specified object	globoid	resembling a globe
13. **ory**	place of or for	observatory	place for observing celestial bodies
14. **ous**	possessing the qualities of, full of	fibrous	possessing the qualities of, or full of, fibers
15. **ry**	art or profession of	chemistry	art or profession of the chemist

BIOLOGY

DIRECTIONS: Read each of the following passages. Choose the BEST answer to each question. Then blacken the space under that number in the answer column. You may go back to the passage as often as necessary to answer the questions.

ANSWERS AND EXPLANATIONS APPEAR AT THE END OF THE CHAPTER

A-1

Scientific terms: barb, barbule, contour feather, dermal covering, diffraction, down, filoplume, follicle, molt, quill, shaft, vane

Modern birds are probably the most distinctive of animals. They are characterized by their feathers, horny beaks, absence of teeth, wings that have developed from primitive forelegs, a four-chambered heart, and warm blood. Birds and mammals are the only animals that maintain a regular body temperature. Their [circulatory] systems feature a thermal control that is generally independent of environmental temperatures and that keeps the body temperature at a nearly constant level.

Unique among birds is the presence of feathers. A feather is similar to a scale in that it is an outgrowth from the dermal covering of the body. Feathers arise in small pits called follicles. The common contour feather consists of a basal portion called the quill, and its extension, which is known as the shaft. There are many fine flexible branches which lead off from the shaft, and these are called barbs. In a further ramification of the barbs are numerous finer branches, called barbules. Barbules on one side of a barb have hooklets that catch the barbules on the next succeeding barb and give a degree of rigidity to the whole blade-like structure, which is then called a vane.

Besides contour feathers, birds have other kinds of feathers which scientists refer to as down and filoplumes. Often, young birds fresh from the egg have only down feathers; the development of contour feathers occurs at a later stage of development. When the contour feathers cover the down feathers, the two together act as an insulating system. The down feathers are able to retain the bird's body heat in a highly efficient manner.

The biggest feathers of birds, and usually the heaviest, are found on the tail and posterior wing margins forming the planes of flight. The overlapping of the feathers, in an orderly and well-designed way, with the tips pointed to the rear, gives rigidity and strength to the wings. It also lessens air resistance and greatly aids in allowing rain to run off the body of the bird.

Feathers arise only from definite surface regions called feather tracts. The feathers are shed periodically in a process called molting. The colors of a bird's plumage usually serve either as a type of camouflage to protect the birds from enemies or as a very bright attraction to lure mates. The hues that one observes are due not only to the pigments deposited in the feathers as they form, but also to the diffraction of light. Diffraction, due to light striking the interlacing barbs and barbules of the vanes, occurs most often in the feathers of the throat and neck, and gives these feathers an iridescent appearance.

Scientific terms defined

barb   A branch of a bird's feather.

barbule   The smallest branch of a bird's feather.

contour feather   One of the outer feathers that cover a bird's body and play a part in giving outward shape to the body.

dermal covering   The outer part of the skin which covers the body of an animal.

diffraction   The spreading or bending of a wave (as a light wave) upon passing around an obstacle or through a narrow opening.

down   A covering of soft, fine feathers on newly hatched birds and under the outer feathers of adult birds.

filoplume   A down feather.

follicle   A small depression in the skin from which a hair or a feather grows.

molt   To shed feathers or hairs periodically.

quill   The thick, stiff, basal, central part of a feather.

shaft   The upper, thinner, stiff, central part of a feather.

vane   The flat expanded part of a feather, made up of interlocking barbs and barbules.

1. In the history of living things, birds developed
    (1)   before four-legged animals.
    (2)   after four-legged animals.
    (3)   at the same time as four-legged animals.
    (4)   none of the above

2. The principal parts of a contour feather are
    (1)   barbs, filoplumes, down, and hooklets.
    (2)   vanes, down, follicles, and barbules.
    (3)   follicles, barbules, filoplumes, and down.
    (4)   quill, shaft, barbs, and barbules.

3. Although some newly hatched birds have both down and some contour feathers, others, the passage says, have only down. Thus, all newly hatched birds have down feathers. This is the case because
   (1) newly hatched birds cannot fly.
   (2) down feathers are needed to retain the newly hatched bird's heat.
   (3) contour feathers would cause the newly hatched bird to take up too much room in the nest.
   (4) down feathers are softer than contour feathers.

   3. 1 2 3 4

4. The iridescent body and tail feathers of a peacock, which is a native of the jungle, were developed for the purpose of
   (1) camouflage from enemies.
   (2) attracting mates.
   (3) aiding flight.
   (4) both (1) and (2) of the above

   4. 1 2 3 4

5. Birds, along with mammals, are known as warm-blooded animals because
   (1) down feathers warm their blood.
   (2) the temperature of their blood is warm when the environment is warm, and cool when the environment is cool.
   (3) their blood maintains an even, relatively warm temperature no matter what the temperature of the environment may be.
   (4) both (1) and (2) of the above

   5. 1 2 3 4

A-2

Scientific terms: biosphere, fungi, isotope, metabolism, nematode, pesticide, radioactive, strontium-90

Strontium-90, like other radioactive isotopes of elements, has probably always existed in the biosphere in small amounts. But recent activities of man, particularly the testing of atomic weapons, have increased the quantity of strontium-90. Chemically, strontium is very much like calcium and is used by organisms in a similar way. But if calcium in an animal is replaced by strontium-90, the replacement releases radiations that harm or kill living tissues. Strontium, like calcium, can be passed from green plants to cows, and from cows' milk to man. But not all the strontium-90 that might be in a cow's food goes into her milk; much of it stays in her own skeleton or passes out as wastes. In fact, the metabolism of a cow discriminates against strontium in synthesizing muscle and milk. The contaminated plants a cow eats contain twice as much strontium as the cow's muscles and seven times as much as her milk. If strontium-90 pollutes the atmosphere, it is obviously safer to drink milk than to eat green vegetables.

Perhaps more dangerous at present than radioactive substances are pesticides. These are poisons that are used to kill pests—that is, organisms that are harmful to man, his domesticated animals, or his crops. Because of the basic similarity in metabolism of all living things, it is difficult to find a substance that is poisonous to one organism and not to another, particularly another closely related one. For example, a substance poisonous to wasps (which might be considered pests) is very likely to be poisonous also to honeybees (which seldom are considered pests).

In the struggle to produce enough food for the growing human population, poisons against many kinds of fungi, nematodes, mites, insects, and other organisms are necessary. But the ever-increasing use of these poisons endangers the biosphere. Some (DDT, for example) are very resistant to chemical change. Therefore, even small amounts of DDT, when used repeatedly, build up to large amounts in soil and water. Further, some poisons are concentrated in the bodies of organisms; DDT accumulates especially in fats. In Clear Lake, California, DDT was applied at the rate of 14, 20, and 20 parts per billion of lake water in 1949, 1954, and 1957, respectively. In 1957, all lake organisms that were tested contained DDT. Fatty tissues of the aquatic birds called grebes that had died from poisoning were found to contain concentrations of DDT 80,000 times greater than that in the lake water. Fat in some fishes showed a concentration of DDT 140,000 times greater than that in the lake water.

Scientific terms defined

biosphere The sphere of all the earth's living organisms which penetrate the lithosphere, hydrosphere, and atmosphere.

fungi A group of simple plants lacking chlorophyll and comprising molds, mildew, rusts, smuts, mushrooms, and others.

isotope Any of two or more forms of the same element having the same number of protons but different numbers of neutrons, thus differing in atomic weight.

metabolism The total natural processes involved in the building up or tearing down of living tissues and also including respiration.

nematode Any of a class of worms, including the pinworm, trichina, round-worm, and many others.

pesticide Any chemical that is used to kill organisms harmful to man, domesti-cated animals, or crops.

radioactive Involved in the process of radioactivity, which is the spontaneous breaking down of the nucleus of an atom during which alpha particles, beta particles, and gamma rays are given off and a new kind of atom is formed as a result.

strontium-90 The radioactive isotope of strontium, with an atomic weight of 90.

6. Although strontium-90 and calcium are chemically similar, the difference that makes strontium-90 a poison is that strontium-90
   (1) replaces calcium in the tissues of living organisms.
   (2) is a pesticide.
   (3) collects in the fatty tissues of organisms.
   (4) is radioactive, releasing radiations that harm or kill living tissues.

6. 1 2 3 4

7. The first stage in the process by which strontium-90 gets into milk is that
   (1) a cow synthesizes strontium-90 in her muscles.
   (2) a green plant synthesizes strontium-90 in its tissues.
   (3) a green plant takes up strontium-90 from its environment.
   (4) both (1) and (2) of the above

7. 1 2 3 4

8. Animals can habitually eat green plants or drink water containing DDT without suffering immediate harm and yet eventually die from DDT poisoning because
   (1) DDT becomes fatal only at certain times of the year.
   (2) DDT collects in the animals' fatty tissues.
   (3) it takes time for a lethal dose of DDT to collect in the fatty tissues.
   (4) both (2) and (3) of the above

8. 1 2 3 4

9. When a cow eats plants contaminated by strontium-90, her metabolism
   (1) passes one-seventh of the strontium-90 into her milk.
   (2) holds back all the strontium-90 from her milk.
   (3) prevents six-sevenths of the strontium-90 from going into her milk.
   (4) both (1) and (3) of the above

9. 1 2 3 4

10.

10. A beekeeper who had an orchard that was invaded by a swarm of wasps would have to be careful in choosing a pesticide for use against the wasps because

(1) the pesticide would probably hurt the apple trees.

(2) a pesticide would accumulate in the fatty tissues of the bees.

(3) a pesticide that killed wasps would probably also kill bees.

(4) none of the above

A-3

Scientific terms: chemosynthesizer, compound, ecological, ecosystem, habitat, inorganic, organic, photosynthesizer

The scientific term ecosystem is used to indicate a natural unit of living and nonliving things interacting to form a somewhat stable system within which energy sources and other materials are exchanged among the various organisms and with the nonliving environment in a kind of cycle. Ecosystems may be studied on a microscopic basis within a droplet of water or a tiny cube of soil, or within a much larger situation such as a large lake or a great forest.

Regardless of its size, an ecosystem may be divided up into: (1) the producers—photosynthesizers and chemosynthesizers [which are plants] that "lock up" radiant energy of light; (2) the consumers—organisms that eat other organisms [both plant and animal]; (3) the decomposers —bacteria and fungi that decompose, or break down, organic compounds of dead [plants and animals] and wastes into inorganic substances which can be reused [by living organisms]; (4) the nonliving environment—surroundings from which the materials for life and growth can be drawn and which act as a reservoir into which they can be returned and used later.

The habitat of an organism is the general type of locality or ecological situation surrounding it. More than one type of organism may live in the same habitat, as many kinds of living things may live together in a swamp, a pond, along a seabeach or lakeshore, or on a hilltop. An ecological niche is the specific place and status of a particular organism within an ecosystem and habitat. This niche must provide all the environmental factors for that organism's survival. It includes such factors as the organism's food sources, other organisms that may prey upon it, its abilities to move about or migrate, and its effect on its nonliving surroundings.

For example, along the shore of a lake, many kinds of organisms live near one another. Each kind plays a different role in the biological economy of this habitat. New species coming into a habitat and establishing themselves can create niches, and new interrelationships may occur.

Scientific terms defined

chemosynthesizer A term that applies to a small number of bacteria that employ the energy released in chemical processes (such as the oxidation of nitrogen and sulfur compounds) to synthesize their protoplasm from entirely inorganic sources.

compound A substance composed of chemically united elements in definite proportions.

ecological   Having to do with the environments of living things or with the patterns of relations between living things and their environments.

ecosystem   A natural unit of living and nonliving things interacting to form a somewhat stable system within which energy sources and other materials are exchanged among various organisms and with the nonliving environment in a kind of cycle.

habitat   The general type of locality or ecological situation surrounding an organism.

inorganic   A substance which is not living nor has ever lived.

organic   (1) A substance which is living or has previously lived; for example, a live tree and a log. (2) In chemistry, the study of carbon compounds—those compounds that contain carbon, usually in combination with hydrogen and/or oxygen.

photosynthesizer   An organism that makes its own food in the form of carbohydrates (usually the sugar, glucose) using the raw materials carbon dioxide and water, energy from light, and the green compound chlorophyll as a catalyst. All photosynthesizers are green plants.

11. Golden plovers migrate from northern Argentina to northern Canada. It is safe to say that in these two locations the plovers have found
   (1)   an environment.
   (2)   an ecological niche.
   (3)   a habitat.
   (4)   both (2) and (3) of the above

12. If a group of antelope were transported from Africa to Antarctica, they would eventually
   (1)   find an ecological niche.
   (2)   become part of an antarctic ecological system.
   (3)   have a new habitat.
   (4)   none of the above

13. A drop of pond water swarming with microscopic organisms and placed on a microscope slide
   (1)   may be considered an ecosystem.
   (2)   is too small to be an ecosystem.
   (3)   is part of an ecosystem.
   (4)   both (1) and (2) of the above

14. Human beings
   (1)   are not part of any ecosystem.
   (2)   are animals that change their ecosystem.
   (3)   have a very limited habitat.
   (4)   none of the above

15. A zoo is
   (1)   a natural ecosystem.
   (2)   an artificial ecosystem.
   (3)   not an ecosystem.
   (4)   none of the above

A-4

Scientific terms: antheridium, archegonium, gametophyte, germinate, spore, sporophyte, zygote

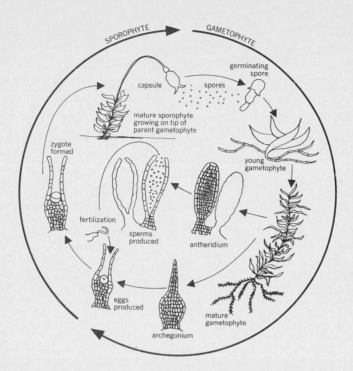

Reproductive cycle of a moss. The parts are drawn to different scales.

This diagram depicts the life, or reproductive, cycle of a moss. The labeled figures represent steps and structures in the cycle. The arrows indicate how the events in the cycle are arranged in time; that is, which events precede or succeed others.

Scientific terms defined

antheridium   The sperm-producing structure of certain simple plants, such as mosses.

archegonium   The egg-producing structure of certain simple plants, such as mosses.

gametophyte   In the alternation of generations of plants, the generation that produces the sex organs.

germinate   To begin to grow or develop, as a seed or spore.

spore   A reproductive cell capable of growing into a mature organism.

sporophyte   In the alternation of generations of plants, the generation that produces the spores.

zygote   A cell formed by the union of two mature sex cells.

16. 1 2 3 4

16. The reproductive cycle of a moss begins with
    (1)   the germinating spore.
    (2)   the production of the eggs.
    (3)   the mature gametophyte.
    (4)   any of the above events.

17. 1 2 3 4

17. The diagram shows that in its life cycle the moss has two main forms. They are
    (1)   mature gametophyte and capsule.
    (2)   germinating spore and produced egg.
    (3)   sporophyte and gametophyte.
    (4)   none of the above

18. 1 2 3 4

18. The gametophyte generation eventually produces two structures that form sex cells. They are
    (1)   the antheridium and the archegonium.
    (2)   a zygote and spores.
    (3)   a germinating spore and a young gametophyte.
    (4)   sperms and eggs.

19. 1 2 3 4

19. In the history of plants, mosses developed hundreds of millions of years before seed plants. The structure in the moss that is equivalent to a seed is the
    (1)   sperm.   (3)   spore.
    (2)   antheridium.   (4)   none of the above

20. 1 2 3 4

20. The first structure produced by a fertilized moss egg is a
    (1)   zygote.   (3)   capsule.
    (2)   sporophyte.   (4)   spore.

A-5

Scientific terms: consumers, producers

A rabbit and a raspberry bush: One is an animal; the other, a plant. One moves around; the other is rooted in a particular place. All of us can tell an animal from a plant, a rabbit from a raspberry bush!

This looks clear enough. But if we try to work out clear and inclusive definitions, we get into trouble. Everyone who has looked into the matter agrees that corals and sponges are animals. Yet they are as fixed in position as any plant. Then there are things called slime molds, which are sometimes classed as plants but do a great deal of creeping about. And in the microscopic world there are many creatures that move about actively, as most animals do, but use the energy of sunlight for building up foods, as do most plants. Presently we find ourselves in a state where we no longer know the difference between *all* plants and *all* animals. . . .

Let us try another way of looking at the matter. The rabbit is hiding under the raspberry bush. This is important, for most animals must have some place to hide, some kind of shelter. Even more important, the rabbit must have food. Rabbits usually do not eat raspberry bushes, though they would not scorn the young shoots in time of need. But rabbits and raspberry bushes do not live alone. Around the raspberry patch are many other kinds of green plants that rabbits like.

We can call such green plants the *producers* of the living world, since they build up foods by using the energy of sunlight, and the rest of the living world depends on this production. Rabbits, which cannot make food in this way, are *consumers*—that is, "eaters." Because they feed directly on the green plants, they are called first-order consumers. Foxes, cats, wolves, hawks . . . eat rabbits. Besides these larger animals, there are fleas in a rabbit's fur, worms in its intestine, and mosquitos seeking out its pink ears. These are second-order consumers. But wolves may also have fleas, which are then third-order consumers. Even higher-order consumers may be found, each order a step farther from the food producers.

Thus, the producers are the basis of a complicated network of consumers.

Scientific terms defined

producers   Green plants, users of the energy in sunlight to build up their own food.

consumers   Eaters of plants or of the eaters of plants or of the eaters of the eaters of plants, etc.

21. 1 2 3 4

21. All carnivores habitually are meat eating animals; therefore they are
    (1) first-order consumers.
    (2) second-order consumers.
    (3) third-order consumers.
    (4) not all classifiable in a single consumer order.

22. 1 2 3 4

22. Bacteria are plants. Single-celled animals, such as amoebas, eat bacteria. Therefore, amoebas are
    (1) producers.   (3) first-order consumers.
    (2) second-order consumers.   (4) none of the above

23. 1 2 3 4

23. All plants can be distinguished from all animals because
    (1) all plants have green leaves.
    (2) plants are fixed in one location.
    (3) plants alone use the energy of sunlight to make foods.
    (4) none of the above

24. 1 2 3 4

24. Human beings are
    (1) first-order consumers.   (3) third-order consumers.
    (2) second-order consumers.   (4) all of the above

25. 1 2 3 4

25. If a rabbit's fleas had fleas, the fleas' fleas would be
    (1) third-order consumers.   (3) second-order consumers.
    (2) first-order consumers.   (4) none of the above

ANSWERS AND EXPLANATIONS

1. **(2)** The first paragraph states that birds' wings developed from primitive forelegs. If birds' ancestors had forelegs, they must have had hind legs; therefore those ancestors were four-legged. Hence, (2) is the correct choice, and the other answers are eliminated logically.

2. **(4)** Paragraph two describes feathers as being made up of quill, shaft, barbs, and barbules. Thus, (4) is the correct answer. The same paragraph notes that feathers arise from follicles, that some barbules have hooklets, and that barbules hooked together form a vane, but none of these are *parts* of a feather. Paragraph three states that down and filoplumes are kinds of feathers, not parts of a contour feather.

3. **(2)** All newly hatched birds need to retain their body heat. Down feathers, paragraph three says, do this in a highly efficient manner. Thus, (2) is the correct answer. While it is true that newly hatched birds cannot fly (1), and that down feathers are softer than contour feathers (4), neither of these answers fits the question, and thus they are not correct. Also, while it is true that contour feathers probably would cause a newly hatched bird to take up more room in a nest (3), no reason is given to believe that room is or is not a problem for newly hatched birds. Thus, (3) is not correct.

4. **(4)** The fifth paragraph says that the coloring of a bird's feathers may serve as camouflage from enemies or to attract mates. The bright colors of a peacock's feathers could (and do) serve as camouflage in the green shadowy environment of the jungle and as an attraction for peahens. Thus, (1) and (2) are true and (4) is the correct answer. Nothing in the passage is said about any connection between color and a bird's ability to fly, and common sense tells us that there is none. Hence, (3) is incorrect.

5. **(3)** The first paragraph says that birds have a system of thermal (heat) control that keeps body temperature at a constant level that is independent of environmental temperatures. Also, the same paragraph says that birds and mammals are the only animals that maintain a regular body temperature. Man is a mammal and his body temperature is usually warmer than that of his environment. These facts are given in choice (3), which is the correct answer. The third paragraph says that down feathers retain body heat, but mammals do not have feathers and are warm-blooded. Hence, the retention of body heat by down cannot be the basis of the term "warm-blooded." Thus, (1) is incorrect. The reasons given for the correct choice reveal (2) as being incorrect.

6. **(4)** The first paragraph explains that the harm done by strontium-90 is due to its radioactivity. Thus, (4) is the correct answer. Although it is true that strontium-90 replaces calcium in living tissues, this fact alone causes no harm to organisms, because, as paragraph one says, the strontium is used in a way similar to calcium. Thus, (1) is not a correct choice. Strontium-90, according to the passage, is not a pesticide (2),

and it is DDT, not strontium-90, that collects in fatty tissue (3). Thus, (2) and (3) are not correct choices.

7. **(3)** The first paragraph says that cows get strontium-90 from green plants. This indicates that the green plants had to take the strontium-90 into their tissues from some source, which could only be their environment. Thus, (3) is the correct answer. To *synthesize* means "to form a whole thing from parts." Since strontium-90 is a chemical element, it cannot be synthesized by chemical processes such as those that make up the metabolism of plants and animals. Thus, (1) and (2) cannot be correct.

8. **(4)** Paragraph three states that large doses of DDT can be fatal to living organisms and that DDT accumulates in animals' fatty tissues. From these facts we can conclude that, in order to kill an animal, DDT must accumulate over a period of time in the animal's fatty tissues. Thus, (2) and (3) are true, making (4) the correct answer. There is nothing in the passage to indicate that (1) might be correct.

9. **(4)** Paragraph one says that the contaminated plants a cow eats contain seven times as much strontium-90 as her milk. Choices (1) and (3) say the same thing in different words. Thus, (4) is the correct answer.

10. **(3)** Paragraph two explains that a substance poisonous to wasps is likely to be poisonous to bees. Thus, (3) is the correct answer. The passage says that DDT collects in the fatty tissues; however, the question does not say that the poison that might be used by the beekeeper would be DDT. Thus, we cannot know whether or not it would collect in the bees' fatty tissues, and (2) is not a correct choice. Not knowing the pesticide in question, we cannot say whether or not it would harm apple trees; hence, (1) cannot be a correct choice.

11. **(4)** Since the plovers live in Canada and Argentina between migrations, these two places provide the general type of locality or ecological situation surrounding the birds. According to paragraph three, such a situation is a habitat. Thus, choice (3) is true. Also, since there must be, in both Canada and Argentina, food sources and animals and birds that prey on the plovers, and since they maintain the ability to migrate and must have an effect on their surroundings—because of all of these things, the plovers have found, according to paragraph three, an ecological niche in both Canada and Argentina. Thus, choice (2) is true. With both (2) and (3) being true, (4) is the correct answer. An organism does not find its environment; the organism is always in some kind of surroundings, which are its environment. Thus, the plovers, even when migrating, are in an environment; hence, (1) is not a correct answer.

12. **(4)** Since antelope are grazing and browsing animals, they would starve in the antarctic, where no grass or trees grow, or they would freeze before starving. They could not accomplish any of the things enumerated in choices (1), (2), or (3), thus making (4) the correct answer.

13. **(3)** A drop of water on a microscope slide would not fulfill the conditions given in paragraph one for an ecosystem. One of the most important of these conditions is stability, and, since a drop of water soon dries up, it is not stable. Thus, (1) is not a correct choice. Paragraph one explains that ecosystems may have different sizes, so a drop of pond water is not disqualified merely by size. Hence, (2) is not correct. According to the definition of an ecosystem given in paragraph one, a pond would be an ecosystem, and a drop of water taken from a pond would be part of an ecosystem. Thus, (3) is the correct answer.

14. **(2)** Human beings qualify very well as being part of an ecosystem as defined in paragraph one. Hence, (1) is not a correct choice. Human beings travel more widely and live in more places than any other animal. Hence, human habitat is not limited, and (3) is incorrect. Human beings, by polluting the atmosphere, lithosphere, and hydrosphere have destroyed many species of animals and threaten the existence of many others. Thus, human beings are animals that change their ecosystem, making (2) the correct answer.

15. **(3)** A zoo is an artificial grouping of animals and therefore is not a natural system of any kind. Hence, (1) is incorrect. Although a zoo is relatively stable, there is no exchange of energy sources and other materials among the animals of the zoo; therefore, they do not form an ecosystem. Thus, (2) is incorrect and (3) is the correct answer.

16. **(4)** A cycle is made up of a series of two or more events that follow in an endless round. Therefore, you cannot pick one event as being first in the reproductive cycle of a moss plant. However, for the purpose of studying the cycle, any event may be picked as a beginning. Thus, (4) is the correct answer.

17. **(3)** The diagram shows by means of the large curving arrows that the life cycle of a moss is divided into two main parts, the sporophyte stage and the gametophyte stage. The list of SCIENTIFIC TERMS DEFINED explains that sporophyte and gametophyte are the two generations in the life of a moss plant. Thus, (3) is the correct answer. Choice (1) gives only one *main* part of the life cycle, and (2) gives no main part. Hence, (1) and (2) are incorrect.

18. **(1)** The mature gametophyte produces two sex structures, an antheridium and an archegonium. Therefore, (1) is the correct answer. (4) is not correct. The sperm and egg are sex cells. The zygote is the cell formed by the union of the sperm and egg. The zygote and spores are in the sporophyte, not the gametophyte generation. Thus, (2) is incorrect. A germinating spore is not a sexual structure, so (3) could not be a correct choice.

19. **(3)** The diagram shows only one structure germinating, and the definition states that a spore is capable of growing into a mature organism. This is the same function as that of a seed. Thus, (3) is the correct answer. Neither the sperm nor the antheridium, according to the diagram, germinates as a seed does. Thus, (1) and (2) are not correct.

20. (1) Fertilization is the union of a sperm and an egg. The diagram shows an open antheridium with sperms produced, and an arrow from this antheridium depicts a sperm moving toward the opened archegonium which contains eggs. The label above this archegonium reads "fertilization." The arrow leading away from the archegonium with fertilized eggs points to a zygote, which is the first structure produced by a fertilized moss egg. Thus, (1) is the correct answer, and all the others must be wrong.

21. (4) Since some carnivores eat other carnivores, a meat-eating animal may be a second-, third-, or higher-order consumer. For, a polar bear may eat a seal which ate a fish that ate a smaller fish; the smaller fish eats algae, which are plants, making the small fish a first-order consumer. The polar bear, then, is a fourth-order consumer, the seal, a third-, etc. Thus, we cannot say that *all* carnivores are definitely in one or the other consumer orders. Hence, (4) is the correct answer. Since first-order consumers are plant-eaters and carnivores do not habitually eat plants, carnivores are not first-order consumers, and (1) is not correct.

22. (3) First-order consumers are plant-eaters; bacteria are plants; amoebas eat bacteria; therefore amoebas are first-order consumers, and (3) is the correct answer.

23. (4) The second paragraph explains that it is not possible to make clear and inclusive definitions that separate plants and animals. It notes that some animals are fixed in one location and some organisms that move about (like most animals) use the energy of sunlight to make their own food. From your experience, you know that some plants, such as mushrooms and toadstools, are not green and do not have leaves. Thus, neither (1), (2), nor (3) is correct, and (4) is the proper answer.

24. (4) Human beings eat plants and therefore are first-order consumers; but human beings also eat plant-eating animals and some meat-eating animals, making human beings second- and third-order consumers, too. Hence, (4) is the correct answer.

25. (1) A rabbit is a first-order consumer; its fleas are second-order consumers. If these fleas had fleas, the fleas' fleas would be third-order consumers. Thus, (1) is the correct answer.

CHEMISTRY

DIRECTIONS: Read each of the following passages. Choose the BEST answer to each question. Then blacken the space under that number in the answer column. You may go back to the passage as often as necessary to answer the questions.

ANSWERS AND EXPLANATIONS APPEAR AT THE END OF THE CHAPTER

B-1

Scientific terms: compound, element, heterogeneous, homogeneous, mixture, solution

On the basis of its chemical composition, matter may be classified as follows:

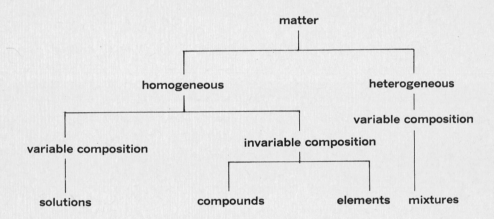

A *homogeneous* material is one which is perfectly uniform in composition—every part is like every other part. Every minute bit of sugar is exactly like every other minute bit of sugar. Materials which are homogeneous are sometimes termed *pure* substances. Salt, soda, aspirin, and gold are further examples of homogeneous, or pure, substances.

Materials which are not uniform in composition are said to be *heterogeneous* or *impure* and are called *mixtures*. Most of the materials we encounter in everyday life are of this type. Food products, wood, rocks, soil, and cement are examples. These materials are mixtures of pure substances.

The constituents of a mixture may be present in different proportions. For example, various cements contain variable proportions of calcium and aluminum silicates. Bread is a mixture of ingredients which may be present in different proportions.

The constituents of a mixture retain their identities because their physical and chemical properties have not been changed by simple mixing—for example, a mixture of powdered iron and powdered sulfur retains the properties of both iron and sulfur. The sulfur, which dissolves in carbon disulfide, may be separated from the iron by extraction with that solvent; the iron, which is attracted to a magnet, may be separated from the sulfur by magnetic attraction.

A *compound* is a pure substance which may be broken down, or decomposed, by chemical means into two or more simpler substances. Water, for example, is a compound substance, since it may be decomposed into hydrogen and oxygen by means of an electric current. Sugar may be decomposed by heat into carbon and water. Baking soda, alum, and salt also are compound substances.

There are a number of substances, however, which have not been decomposed into simpler substances by ordinary chemical means. For example, such familiar substances as iron, copper, gold, sulfur, oxygen, hydrogen, and tin have not been decomposed. These substances are called elements. . . .

We have all observed that sugar dissolves in water to form a clear *solution*. The sugar distributes itself uniformly throughout the liquid so that every part of the solution is exactly like every other part. In other words, a solution is homogeneous. We know, too, that the amount of sugar that will dissolve in a given amount of water is variable; we may dissolve a teaspoonful or a cup of sugar in a pint of water. Solutions, then, are like compounds in that they are homogeneous, but they are unlike compounds and like mixtures in that the proportion of constituents is variable.

Scientific terms defined

compound A homogeneous substance made up of two or more chemical elements combined in fixed and invariable proportion by weight.

element A substance that cannot be decomposed into simpler substances by chemical means.

heterogeneous In chemistry, substances that are not uniform in composition; impure.

homogeneous In chemistry, substances that are uniform in composition; pure.

mixture In chemistry, a material not uniform in composition.

solution A homogeneous mixture of two or more substances, the relative proportions of which may be varied within certain limits.

1.   ¹   2   3   4

1. If you dissolve two teaspoonfuls of salt in a glass of water, and four teaspoonfuls in another glass, then thoroughly mix the two solutions, the resulting liquid material will be
   (1) a mixture.   (3) homogeneous.
   (2) a solution.   (4) both (2) and (3) of the above

2. If you put some white powder of unknown identity into water and found that some of it dissolved but the rest would not dissolve no matter how much water you used, you would know that the powder originally was a(n)

   (1) compound.   (3) element.
   (2) mixture.   (4) solution.

3. If you have some grains of a material and find that they dissolve in water, this test will help you determine whether the material is

   (1) a compound.   (3) a mixture.
   (2) of variable composition.   (4) none of the above

4. If you wanted to know whether a sample of a powder is a homogeneous or a heterogeneous material, a *good first step* would be to

   (1) find out if it will dissolve in water or some other solvent.
   (2) weigh it.
   (3) run it through a sieve.
   (4) grind it fine.

5. A solution and a mixture both are

   (1) of variable composition.
   (2) homogeneous.
   (3) matter.
   (4) both (1) and (3) of the above

B-2

Scientific terms: anisotopic, atomic number, atomic weight unit (awu), cyclotron, hypothesis, isotopes, mass spectrograph, mono-nuclidic, neutron, proton, Van de Graaff accelerator.

[The atomic weight of a chemical element is a quantity equal to the average of the weights of the atoms that make up that element. Atomic weights are relative, since we assign an atom a certain weight (depending upon the number of protons and neutrons in its nucleus) in comparison with the weight of an atom of the element carbon, carbon-12. The atomic weight of carbon-12 is set arbitrarily at exactly 12.]

The idea that atomic weights of all elements should be whole numbers was first suggested by William Prout about 1815. He suspected that all elements might be multiples of hydrogen atoms. The atomic weight of a hydrogen atom is about one [atomic weight unit, or] awu. If this idea were true, therefore, all atomic weights would be (very nearly) whole numbers. But as atomic weights were determined more and more accurately, it became evident that many of them certainly are not whole numbers. Conservative scientists, therefore, laughed at Prout's idea. Little did they realize how close his hypothesis had come to a fundamental idea about the structure of atoms—a structure not discovered until [nearly a century] later.

About 1910, Prout's idea was revived by an English scientist, Frederick Soddy. He suggested that all atomic weights would be very nearly whole numbers if elements like chlorine (Cl = 35.45 awu) were considered as mixtures of two kinds of atoms.

Shortly after this astounding prediction, two different kinds of chlorine atoms were discovered by the use of a mass spectrograph. They were found to have atomic weights of 34.97 awu and 36.97 awu. These two different kinds of chlorine atoms have the same atomic number and have practically identical chemical properties. They differ only in atomic weights. Such atoms are called isotopes. The word isotope means occupying the same or equal (*iso*) place (*topos*). They occupy the same space in the periodic table and the electron chart.

Since all nuclei of a given element must have the same number of protons, any differences in their weights must be due to a difference in the numbers of neutrons in these nuclei. The isotope Cl^{35} has 17 protons and 18 neutrons, while Cl^{37} has 17 protons and 20 neutrons. Thus, isotopes are atoms differing from each other only in the number of neutrons in the nucleus.

More than 60 elements have been shown to be mixtures of isotopes, as chlorine is. The number of isotopes for different elements runs from 2 to 10. Altogether, more than 1500 isotopes are known. Many of them have been made artificially in "atom-smashing" devices, such as cyclotrons and Van de Graaff accelerators, while many others are prepared in nuclear reactors.

About 20 elements have not as yet been found to have natural isotopes. So far as is known, each of these elements consists of only one kind of atom and is said to be "anisotopic," or "mono-nuclidic." A few of these are fluorine, sodium, phosphorus, arsenic, aluminum, iodine, and gold.

Scientific terms defined

anisotopic   Having no natural isotopes.

atomic number   A number equal to the number of protons within the nucleus of an element. The atomic number determines the place of the element in the periodic table.

atomic weight unit (**awu**)   The unit in which atomic weights are designated, equal to one-twelfth the weight of carbon-12.

cyclotron   A device that uses magnetic means to accelerate heavy atomic particles, such as protons; one kind of "atom smasher."

hypothesis   A theory or supposition tentatively adopted to guide investigation or explain certain facts.

isotopes   Atoms of the same element having the same number of protons, but different numbers of neutrons in the nucleus.

mass spectrograph   An apparatus for determining the weights of atoms by analyzing positively charged rays of atoms or molecules.

mono-nuclidic   Anisotopic.

neutron   A fundamental atomic particle having no electrical charge and a mass of one.

proton   A fundamental atomic particle having a positive electrical charge and a mass of one.

Van de Graaff accelerator   An atomic accelerator using static electricity as the accelerating force.

6. The chlorine isotope that has an atomic weight of (approximately) 35 has 17 protons and 18 neutrons in its nucleus. Assume that a proton has a weight of 1.0. From this data, we can say that the atomic weight of a neutron when compared to the atomic weight of a proton is
   (1) greater.
   (2) less.
   (3) the same.
   (4) none of the above

   6. 1   2   3   4

7. Atoms of an element are called isotopes when they differ from each other
   (1) in the number of protons in the nucleus.
   (2) in the number of neutrinos in the nucleus.
   (3) only in the number of electrons in the nucleus.
   (4) only in the number of neutrons in the nucleus.

   7. 1   2   3   4

8. 1 2 3 4

8. According to the passage, a sample of chlorine has an atomic weight of 35.45 and its isotopes have atomic weights of 34.97 and 36.97. The sample, therefore, must have
   (1)   a greater proportion of the lighter isotope.
   (2)   a smaller proportion of the lighter isotope.
   (3)   a smaller proportion of the heavier isotope.
   (4)   both (1) and (3) of the above

9. 1 2 3 4

9. A certain element is a mixture of two isotopes, 50% of which have an atomic weight of 98 and the remaining 50% have an atomic weight of 100. The atomic weight of a sample of the element is
   (1)   99.   (3)   97.
   (2)   99.5.   (4)   98.5.

10. 1 2 3 4

10. Elements may be identified by their atomic numbers. The atomic number of chlorine is 17. From these facts you can deduce that the number of protons in the nucleus is
   (1)   1.   (3)   35.45.
   (2)   17.   (4)   none of the above.

B-3

Scientific terms: electrochemical, electromotive, ion, oxidation, potential, reduction

[When any metal takes part in a chemical reaction in which the metal loses electrons the process is called *oxidation* and the metal is said to be oxidized. Along with the loss in electrons there is an equivalent gain of electrons by the other element in the reaction. This gain is called *reduction* and the element that gains the electrons is said to be reduced. A metallic atom that is neither oxidized nor reduced is said to be *neutral,* and is indicated by a raised zero, thus, Zn^0. Electrons are electrically negative, or minus, charges. The loss of electrons by the atom of an oxidized metal leaves the atom with a net positive, or plus, charge and is indicated by raised plus signs, thus, Cu^{++}. Conversely, in reduction, the atom that gains the electrons has a net negative charge and is indicated by raised minus signs, thus, Cl^-. Atoms that have net electric charges are called *ions*.]

[When a neutral atom, such as Zn^0, reacts with an ion, such as Cu^{++}, the Zn^0 loses two electrons and becomes oxidized to a Zn^{++} ion. Meanwhile the Cu^{++} ion gains the two electrons and becomes reduced to a neutral Cu^0 atom.]

Electromotive Series

(only the more familiar metals are listed)

K (potassium)
Ba (barium)
Ca (calcium)
Na (sodium)
Mg (magnesium)
Al (aluminum)
Mn (manganese)
Zn (zinc)
Cr (chromium)
Fe (iron)
Co (cobalt)
Ni (nickel)
Sn (tin)
Pb (lead)
H (hydrogen)
Sb (antimony)
Bi (bismuth)
Cu (copper)
Hg (mercury)
Ag (silver)
Pt (platinum)
Au (gold)

Zn^0 atoms react with Cu^{++} ions because zinc is a more active metal than copper; similarly, Pb^0 atoms react with Cu^{++} ions because lead is the more active. The activity of a metal is measured by the ease with which it loses electrons to form positive ions. The relative activities of two reacting metals such as zinc and copper or lead and copper provide the driving force for the reactions. . . . All metals can be listed in the order of their activities as compared to other metals and hydrogen; this list is called the **electromotive series.** [It lists the most active metal at the top; the least active at the bottom.] Since zinc atoms lose electrons and easily become positively charged ions, zinc is placed relatively high in the electromotive series. Lead is placed much lower than zinc because lead loses electrons much less readily than zinc does. Copper is placed low in the series; when reacting with a more active metal, copper ions gain electrons. Copper atoms can lose electrons, but much less readily than zinc atoms.

The energy required to remove electrons from metallic atoms varies from element to element. The metals are arranged according to the ease with which electrons can be removed. The removal of electrons becomes more difficult in elements progressively lower in the series.

Scientific terms defined

electrochemical Pertaining to (1) the use of an electric current to cause chemical changes, and (2) generation of electric current by chemical change.

electromotive Pertaining to, tending to produce, or producing a flow of electricity.

ion An atom or group of atoms possessing an electric charge.

oxidation In chemistry, a process involving loss of electrons by an atom or group of atoms.

potential, or **potential difference** The difference in energy (measured in volts) that determines the tendency of an electric charge to move, or an electric current to flow, from one point to another.

reduction In chemistry, a process involving gain of electrons by an atom or group of atoms.

11. 1 2 3 4

11. In the electromotive series, if metal x is more active than metal y,
    (1) x will appear above hydrogen, y below.
    (2) both will appear above hydrogen.
    (3) metal x will appear above metal y.
    (4) metal x will appear below metal y.

12. 1 2 3 4

12. Acids contain hydrogen (H^+) ions. For example, hydrochloric acid is made up of hydrogen and chlorine (H^+Cl^-). If you put a pure silver ring into hydrochloric acid, the ring would be unharmed because
    (1) silver is too tough to be harmed by acid.
    (2) Ag^0 is too far below hydrogen to react with H^+.
    (3) electrons can very easily be removed from Ag^0.
    (4) none of the above

13. 1 2 3 4

13. Which of the following is true?
    (1) Chromium is more active than tin and zinc.
    (2) Copper is less active than silver and iron.
    (3) Mercury is less active than nickel and gold.
    (4) Iron is more active than lead and gold.

14. 1 2 3 4

14. Basing your answer on the first sentence of paragraph three of the passage and an inspection of the electromotive series,
    (1) Zn^0 (zinc) atoms will react with Pb^{++} (lead) ions.
    (2) Zn^0 atoms will not react with Pb^{++} ions.
    (3) Zn is more active than Pb.
    (4) both (1) and (3) of the above

15. 1 2 3 4

15. Of those metals listed in the electromotive series, the one that oxidizes most easily is
    (1) hydrogen.   (3) gold
    (2) potassium.   (4) antimony.

B-4

Scientific terms: molecule, reaction

Consider the reaction between H_2 (hydrogen) and I_2 (iodine) gases. If the same number of molecules of H_2 and I_2 are placed in a fixed-volume container at a constant temperature, the reaction proceeds at a certain rate that depends on the collision frequency between the molecules of the two kinds of gases. Since the volume is fixed, the concentration can be changed by adding more H_2 or I_2; the reaction rate would then be changed. If the volume were not fixed, reducing it would result in an increase in pressure, thus changing the concentration and resulting in a higher reaction rate.

Experiments show that in the reaction between H_2 and I_2, if the concentration of either reactant is doubled, the reaction rate doubles; or if the concentrations of both reactants are doubled, the reaction rate becomes four times as great. From these results you can conclude that at a constant temperature and volume, the rate for the reaction between H_2 and I_2 is proportional to the concentrations of each of the reactants.

If pieces of zinc and iron of equal size and shape are put into identical solutions of hydrochloric acid, the zinc reacts more vigorously because it is chemically more active than iron. But if this same piece of iron were powdered and then added to the acid solution, it would react more rapidly than the zinc. Why is this "state of division" significant? Powdering the iron increases the surface area of the iron, which provides greater opportunity for contact between the reacting particles. Thus, an increase in surface area gives the same effect as an increase in concentration.

How can you explain the observation that a small lump of sulfur burns at a much faster rate in pure oxygen than in air? The sulfur is in the solid state and its atoms are unable to move freely; therefore, the number of oxygen molecules that contact the surface of the sulfur will largely determine the rate for this reaction. Since only about one fifth of the air is oxygen (by volume), the number of O_2 molecules in pure oxygen is about five times as great as in an equal volume of air. Therefore, the collision frequency increases and results in a greater rate of reaction.

You can see that concentration (including surface area and state of division) is an important rate-determining factor. However, you should be careful in making generalizations about any factor involved in reaction rates. The true effects of any factor on a reaction rate can be determined only by controlled experiments.

Scientific terms defined

molecule   The smallest unit of an element or compound which can exist by itself in a free state.

reaction   A chemical change, one that converts substances into other substances.

16. 1 2 3 4

16. If the amounts of H_2 and I_2 in a container are each halved, the reaction rate will
    (1) be halved.
    (2) remain the same.
    (3) be reduced to one-fourth of the original.
    (4) double.

17. 1 2 3 4

17. If the temperature and volume are kept constant, the rate of reaction between H_2 and I_2 will
    (1) be doubled when the concentrations of both gases are doubled.
    (2) be proportional to the concentrations of each of the gases.
    (3) remain constant.
    (4) vary inversely as the concentrations of H_2 and I_2.

18. 1 2 3 4

18. A lump of sulfur burns much faster in pure oxygen than in air because the
    (1) collision frequency of oxygen and sulfur molecules is greater in pure oxygen.
    (2) state of division of the sulfur accelerates the reaction rate.
    (3) pure oxygen increases the pressure.
    (4) both (2) and (3) of the above

19. 1 2 3 4

19. Some early rocket propellants were powders; some modern propellants are cast as a single solid mass. The modern propellant will burn
    (1) faster.
    (2) slower.
    (3) at the same rate.
    (4) at a rate that cannot be determined from the data given in the question.

20. 1 2 3 4

20. You have a cubic space two inches on each edge and filled with H_2 and I_2. You squeeze the space down to a cube one inch on an edge. If the temperature is kept the same, the reaction rate will
    (1) increase by a factor of eight.
    (2) quadruple.
    (3) triple.
    (4) double.

B-5

Scientific terms: salt, solubility

Although the solubility of a solid in a liquid usually increases with an increase in temperature, this is not always true. The solubilities of several salts in water are shown in [the table] and represented graphically in [the figure].

TABLE: Solubility of Salts at Various Temperatures (g. / 100 g. H_2O)

TEMPERA-TURE °C.	POTASSIUM NITRATE	SODIUM CHLORIDE	POTASSIUM ALUM	CALCIUM CHROMATE	POTASSIUM CHLORIDE	SODIUM SULFATE	SODIUM NITRATE
0	13	35.7	4	13	28	4.8	73
10	21	35.8	10	12		9.0	80
20	31	36	15	10.4	34	19.5	85
30	45	36.3	23	9.4		40.9	92
40	64	36.6	31	8.5	40	48.8	98
50	86	37	49	7.3		46.7	104
60	111	37.3	67	6	46	45.3	
70	139	37.9	101	5.3		44.4	
80		38.4	135	4.4	51	43.7	133
90		39.1		3.8		43.1	
100	249	39.8		3	57	42.5	163

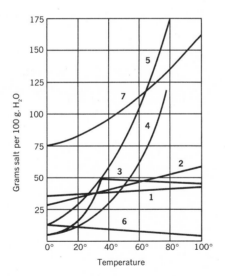

Figure: Solubility curves. (1) NaCl; (2) KCl; (3) Na₂SO₄; (4) alum; (5) KNO₃; (6) CaCrO₄; (7) NaNO₃.

Scientific terms defined

salt   In chemistry, a compound formed by the combination of an acid and a base, by the replacement of the hydrogen of an acid with a metal, and by certain other reactions.

solubility The amount of a substance that will dissolve in a given amount of another substance.

21. 1 2 3 4

21. If you are dissolving table salt (sodium chloride, NaCl) in water, raising the temperature will increase the amount of salt you can dissolve in a given amount of water
(1) greatly.
(3) slightly.
(2) not at all.
(4) none of the above

22. 1 2 3 4

22. If you were trying to increase the amount of calcium chromate ($CaCrO_4$) you could dissolve in water, you would do well to
(1) raise the temperature.
(2) lower the temperature.
(3) keep the temperature constant.
(4) none of the above

23. 1 2 3 4

23. If you were dissolving sodium sulfate (Na_2SO_4) in water, the best temperature for the water would be closest to
(1) 40°C.
(3) 98°C.
(2) 52°C.
(4) 4°C.

(*Hint:* Check *both* table and curve.)

24. 1 2 3 4

24. The greatest increase in dissolved material due to increase in temperature will be obtained when dissolving
(1) potassium nitrate (KNO_3).
(3) potassium chloride (KCl).
(2) potassium alum.
(4) sodium nitrate ($NaNO_3$).

25. 1 2 3 4

25. As a *general rule*, as the temperature of water rises, the amount of a compound that can be dissolved
(1) decreases.
(3) remains the same.
(2) increases.
(4) is little affected.

ANSWERS AND EXPLANATIONS

1. **(4)** The last paragraph says that sugar dissolves completely in water to form homogeneous matter called a solution. The question describes an unusual way of dissolving a total of six teaspoonfuls of sugar in a total of two glasses of water. However, the method still makes a sugar solution, which is homogeneous. Thus, choices (2) and (3) are true, and (4) is the correct answer.

2. **(2)** Since some of the powder dissolved and some did not, you would know that it was made up of at least two different materials, and therefore was heterogeneous. According to the diagram and paragraph four, a heterogeneous material is a mixture. Thus, (2) is the correct answer. According to the scheme of the diagram, the fact that a material is heterogeneous eliminates the possibility that it could be either a compound or an element. Thus, (1) and (3) could not be correct.

3. **(4)** The fact that the material dissolves in water does not provide you with any information useful in answering the question because many compounds dissolve and many mixtures of compounds dissolve. Therefore, you could not use this method to decide between a compound and a mixture of compounds. Hence, (1) and (3) cannot be correct. Further, according to the chart, mixtures, which are of variable composition, can be made up of compounds which are of invariable composition. Therefore, the fact that a material dissolves gives no clue about whether it is of variable or of invariable composition. Hence, (2) cannot be correct. Since neither (1), (2), nor (3) is correct, (4) is the correct answer.

4. **(1)** If you try to find out whether the powder will dissolve in an unlimited amount of some solvent, and some of the powder dissolves and some does not, you know that you have a heterogeneous material. If, however, all of the powder dissolves, you will not know whether the powder is homogeneous or heterogeneous, because the powder could be a mixture (which is heterogeneous) of two soluble compounds (each of which is homogeneous). However, attempting to dissolve the powder is a *good first step*, because one result (some of it dissolving, some not) can eliminate the need for further steps. Thus, (1) is the correct answer. Neither weighing it (2), running it through a sieve (3), nor grinding it (4) would make any changes in the powder that would provide information on whether it was homogeneous or heterogeneous. Thus, (2), (3), and (4) cannot be correct.

5. **(4)** The diagram shows that solutions and mixtures both are matter of variable composition. The passage repeats this fact. Thus, (1) and (3) are true, and (4) is the correct answer. The diagram shows that solutions and mixtures do not have in common the property of homogeneity. Thus, (2) cannot be correct.

6. **(3)** The 17 protons of chlorine-35 give an atomic weight of 17 (17 $\times$ 1) awu. Therefore, the neutrons must provide the remaining 18 awu. Hence, the weight of a neutron also is 1.0. Thus, protons and neutrons

have the same atomic weight, and (3) is the correct answer. (Actually, protons and neutrons differ in weight by a little more than one-thousandth of an atomic weight unit; however, since the problem considered only one decimal place, the answer is correct.)

7. **(4)** Paragraph four states that when atoms of the same element differ in weight, the difference must be due to the number of neutrons in the nuclei, and that isotopes are atoms differing from each other only in the number of neutrons in the nucleus. Thus (4) is the correct answer. Paragraph four states that all nuclei of an element must have the same number of protons; therefore (1) cannot be correct. A neutrino is not the same as a neutron; it is a particle with much less weight (mass) than an electron and is electrically neutral. Hence, (2) is not correct. Electrons are normally not found in the nucleus of an atom. Thus, (3) is incorrect.

8. **(4)** If there were 50% of each isotope, the average atomic weight would be 35.97 [(34.97 + 36.97) ÷ 2]. To bring the average down to the actual atomic weight of 35.45, there must be a greater proportion of the lighter isotope (1) or a smaller proportion of the heavier isotope (3). With (1) and (3) being true, (4) is the correct answer.

9. **(1)** Since there is 50% of each of the two isotopes, the atomic weight of a sample of the element is the simple average of the weights of the two isotopes. Then, (100 + 98) ÷ 2 = 99. Thus, (1) is the correct answer.

10. **(2)** According to the definition of the term atomic number, which is given under "Science terms defined" on page 53, (2) is the correct answer. The atomic number is a number equal to the number of protons within the nucleus. Since the atomic number of chlorine is 17, there must be 17 protons within the nucleus of a chlorine atom. (There are also 17 electrons orbiting the nucleus of the chlorine atom. In a neutral atom, the number of protons and of electrons are equal.) The atomic number of an atom does not vary from isotope to isotope.

11. **(3)** The third paragraph of the passage explains that the electromotive series lists metals in order of their activity from top to bottom. Thus, if metal x is more active than metal y, x will appear above y. Hence, (3) is the correct answer. Metal x and metal y may both appear above hydrogen or both may appear below. Thus, (1) is incorrect. That one metal is more active than another gives no clue as to the absolute location of the two metals in the electromotive series. Thus, (2) is not correct. Since (3) is correct, (4) must be incorrect.

12. **(2)** Choice (1) does not explain anything, but simply restates the last sentence of the question in other words. Inspection of the electromotive series shows that Ag (silver) is below hydrogen. Paragraph two states that when a neutral metal atom takes part in a reaction, it loses electrons. And paragraph four says that removal of electrons from metals low in the electromotive series is difficult. Silver (Ag) is third from the bottom, so removal of its electrons in order to enter into a reaction with

the H$^+$ ion of hydrochloric acid is very difficult, so much so that the silver of the ring will not lose electrons to the H$^+$ ion, and the ring will be unharmed. Thus, (2) is the correct answer. Choice (3) states the opposite of the fact stated in paragraph four; hence, (3) is incorrect.

13. **(4)** Inspection of the electromotive series reveals that only (4) is a correct answer, because iron is higher on the electromotive series than both lead and gold.

14. **(4)** From the first sentence of paragraph three you can deduce that a more active atom will react with a less active ion. From the electromotive series, you can deduce that Zn (zinc) is more active than Pb (lead) (3). Therefore, a Zn$^°$ atom will react with a Pb ion (1). With (1) and (3) true, (4) is the correct answer.

15. **(2)** You can learn from the first paragraph that an element that oxidizes loses electrons. The last paragraph states that the removal of electrons becomes more difficult in elements progressively lower in the series; that is, the lower the element, the harder it is to oxidize. Conversely, the higher the element in the series, the more easily it oxidizes. Potassium (K) is at the top of the series and therefore is the one that oxidizes most easily. Thus, (2) is the correct answer.

16. **(3)** If, as stated in paragraph two, the reaction rate is proportional to the concentration of the reactants, and doubling the concentrations of both reactants causes the reaction rate to increase fourfold, then it is a logical deduction that halving the concentrations of both reactants will lower the reaction rate to one fourth of the original. Thus, (3) is the correct answer.

17. **(2)** The last sentence of paragraph two states choice (2) directly; thus (2) is the correct answer. Paragraph two also states that when the concentrations of both gases is doubled, the reaction rate is quadrupled. Thus, (1) is incorrect. When you say that a reaction rate remains constant, you must say or imply at what level or amount it remains constant. Therefore, simply to say that a rate remains constant as in choice (3) is meaningless. If the reaction rate varied inversely as the concentrations of the reactants, when the concentration was increased, the reaction rate would decrease. Paragraphs one and two explain that the opposite is true; the reaction rate, then, is directly proportional to the concentration of the reactants. Thus, (4) is incorrect.

18. **(1)** Paragraph four explains that the lump of sulfur burns much faster in pure oxygen because of the increased collision rate of oxygen and sulfur molecules. Thus, (1) is the correct answer. A single lump of sulfur is involved in the problem; therefore, state of division does not enter directly into the sulfur and oxygen reaction. Hence, (2) is not a correct choice. The purity of the oxygen has nothing to do with pressure. Thus, (3) is incorrect.

19. **(4)** Since the powder is in a greater state of division, you would, according to paragraph four, expect it to burn more rapidly. However, the last

paragraph explains that generalizations on reaction rates cannot be made with certainty, and only experimenting will give a certain answer. Thus, (4) is the correct answer.

20. (1) Paragraph one explains that reducing volume increases pressure and results in a higher reaction rate. A cube 2 inches on an edge has a volume of 8 cubic inches (2 in × 2 in × 2 in = 8 cu in). A cube 1 inch on a side has a volume of only 1 cubic inch (1 in × 1 in × 1 in = 1 cu in). Therefore, the volume is decreased by a factor of 8, and, if all other things remain equal, you should expect an increase of 8 times in the concentration of reactants. This will result in increasing the reaction rate by a factor of 8. Thus, (1) is the correct answer.

21. (3) The table shows that only 4.1 grams more of sodium chloride can be dissolved in 100 grams of water at 100° C than at 0° C. Therefore, sodium chloride is only a little more soluble at higher temperatures. Thus, (3) is the correct answer.

22. (2) The table and the solubility curves show that more calcium chromate dissolves in water at 0° C than at 100° C. Therefore, you would do well to lower the temperature of the water in which you were dissolving calcium chromate. Hence, (2) is the correct answer.

23. (1) The curve indicates that the amount of sodium sulfate that can be dissolved in water increases up to a temperature of about 33° C; then, as the temperature continues to increase, the amount of sodium sulfate that can be dissolved decreases. Therefore, 40° C would be the best temperature at which to dissolve the most sodium sulfate. Hence, (1) is the correct answer.

24. (1) The table shows that between 0° C and 100° C there is an increase of 236 grams of potassium nitrate that can be dissolved. This is the greatest increase shown by any of the compounds listed, and is borne out by the sharply rising curve of KNO_3. Thus, (1) is the correct answer.

25. (2) The table and the curves show that for most of the compounds listed, an increase in water temperature means an increase in the amount of compound that dissolves.

PHYSICS

DIRECTIONS: Read each of the following passages. Choose the BEST answer to each question. Then blacken the space under that number in the answer column. You may go back to the passage as often as necessary to answer the questions.

ANSWERS AND EXPLANATIONS APPEAR AT THE END OF THE CHAPTER

C-1

Scientific terms: none

The ancient Greeks advanced several theories about the nature of light. One of them is of particular interest. According to the theory, light is something that streams out of the eyes much like water out of a hose, the idea being that we see a thing by directing this stream of light to hit it. Thereby we learn what it looks like, much as we learn what a thing feels like by feeling it with our hands. A blind man's eyes emit no light; for this reason he cannot see. . . .

Until the intellectual awakening in Europe known as the Renaissance, this theory was never seriously challenged. Sir Isaac Newton was one of the first to advance a consistent theory of light based upon observation and experiment.

In formulating a theory of light, Newton considered two hypotheses: one, that light is matter; the other, that it is wave energy. Knowing the ability of sound and water waves to bend around a corner, which light seemingly does not do because we cannot see around a corner, Newton rejected the theory of waves in favor of the theory of matter.

According to Newton, light consists of small particles (corpuscles) of matter emitted in all directions in straight lines, or rays, by a luminous body such as the sun, a burning candle, or a red-hot coal. If these rays consisting of corpuscles strike our eyes, we see the source of them. . . .

About the same time that Newton proposed the corpuscular theory, Christian Huygens (1629–1695), a Dutch astronomer and physicist, advanced the wave theory of light. The farther a wave front is from the source, the more nearly a short section of it approaches a straight line, and the more nearly two wave fronts become parallel. Such waves are known as parallel waves.

Light waves coming directly from a source, or from a body which reflects them, cause the sensation of sight, just as Newton claimed for the corpuscles.

Let us suppose that Newton and Huygens had met for the purpose

65

of each scientist arguing for his theory. Newton would not accept the wave theory. He argued that "Sound, which is a wave motion, will travel through a crooked hollow pipe, bend around a hill or other obstruction and be heard. If light is a wave, it too should do the same, but experiment proves that it doesn't."

In reply, Huygens said, "That is not a convincing argument. Take short water waves on a river striking the side of a ship; the waves originating on one side will not be seen on the other. However, if the waves are large and the obstacle is small, the waves will bend around the obstacle and be seen on the other side." Huygens even went so far with this line of reasoning as to predict that a very small obstruction would cast no shadow in light.

[Modern science accepts the theories of both Newton and Huygens, since light acts in some situations as if it were made up of corpuscles called photons and in other situations as if it were made up of waves.]

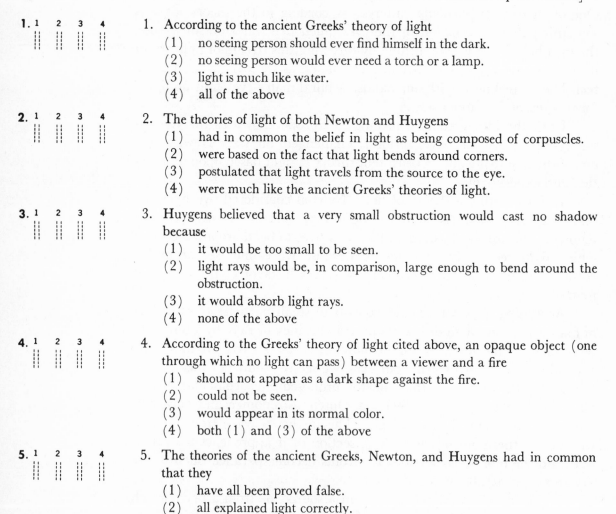

1. According to the ancient Greeks' theory of light
   (1)   no seeing person should ever find himself in the dark.
   (2)   no seeing person would ever need a torch or a lamp.
   (3)   light is much like water.
   (4)   all of the above

2. The theories of light of both Newton and Huygens
   (1)   had in common the belief in light as being composed of corpuscles.
   (2)   were based on the fact that light bends around corners.
   (3)   postulated that light travels from the source to the eye.
   (4)   were much like the ancient Greeks' theories of light.

3. Huygens believed that a very small obstruction would cast no shadow because
   (1)   it would be too small to be seen.
   (2)   light rays would be, in comparison, large enough to bend around the obstruction.
   (3)   it would absorb light rays.
   (4)   none of the above

4. According to the Greeks' theory of light cited above, an opaque object (one through which no light can pass) between a viewer and a fire
   (1)   should not appear as a dark shape against the fire.
   (2)   could not be seen.
   (3)   would appear in its normal color.
   (4)   both (1) and (3) of the above

5. The theories of the ancient Greeks, Newton, and Huygens had in common that they
   (1)   have all been proved false.
   (2)   all explained light correctly.
   (3)   considered light to be a kind of motion.
   (4)   none of the above

C-2

Scientific terms: alloy, lodestone, magnetic pole, magnetism

Magnetism has been known for centuries. Naturally magnetized pieces of iron ore, known as lodestones, were used to perform the seemingly magic feat of picking up iron rings without any visible means of attachment. And slivers of lodestone were used by ancient Greek sailors as crude compasses.

The fact most commonly known about a magnet is that it attracts needles, tacks, nails, iron filings, and other objects made of steel or iron. But a magnet does not attract wood, paper, stone, and most other materials. However, a magnet will attract the metals cobalt and nickel; also alloys (mixtures) of copper, silicon, tin, manganese, and other metals that are not attracted to a magnet separately.

An important fact about a magnet is that when it is dipped into iron filings, paper clips, or tacks they cling to the ends of the magnet, known as its poles, and not around its middle.

Another thing most people know about a magnet is that if it is suspended by its middle so that it can swing freely, it points in a north-south direction. A piece of magnetic material free to rotate is called a compass. The end of the compass that points north is called the north-seeking pole (or simply north pole, or N-pole); the other end is the south-seeking pole (or south pole, or S-pole).

When we bring a north pole of a magnet near the north pole of a freely suspended magnet, the north pole of the suspended magnet is repelled. When two south poles are brought together, they too repel each other. But a north and a south pole brought together attract. From these facts we can deduce a law of physics:

Like magnetic poles repel; unlike poles attract.

This is the Law of Magnetic Poles.

This law gives us a clue to why a compass points as it does. Since the north pole of the magnet points to the geographic north, perhaps there is an unlike magnetic pole in that direction. Investigation has shown that this actually is the case. Near the geographic North Pole there is a magnetic pole, and there is a similar magnetic pole near the earth's South Pole.

Surprisingly, if a magnet is cut in two, we do not get one half with a north pole and one half with a south pole. Instead, we get two complete magnets, each with a north and south pole oriented in the same directions as the poles of the original magnet. If the two new magnets are cut in two, we get four complete magnets. How far can we continue this process? Down to the smallest particle that preserves the characteristics of the metal—the molecule. And, in fact, magnetized material is made up of molecules lined up so that all their north poles point in one direction and all their south poles point in the opposite direction.

Scientific terms defined

alloy   A solution or mixture of two or more metals, the combination having properties different from those of the metals that make it up.

lodestone   A natural magnet; a piece of magnetic iron ore known as magnetite.

magnetic pole   One of the two regions of a magnet where the magnetism seems to be concentrated.

magnetism   The effect of certain substances to attract or repel certain other substances as a result of the arrangement of molecules in these substances.

6.   Magnetism
  (1)   is one of the great discoveries of the twentieth century.
  (2)   has been known since ancient times.
  (3)   was invented by Greek mariners.
  (4)   is a product of ancient magic.

7.   The Law of Magnetic Poles tells us that
  (1)   two north poles repel each other.
  (2)   two south poles repel each other.
  (3)   a north and a south pole attract each other.
  (4)   all of the above

8.   The north pole of a compass
  (1)   is really a north-seeking pole.
  (2)   will repel the north pole of a magnet.
  (3)   is repelled by the earth's south magnetic pole.
  (4)   all of the above

9.   You have a magnet with its north pole at your left and its south pole at your right. You cut the magnet in half. The north poles of the two new magnets now will be
  (1)   at your right.   (3)   in the middle.
  (2)   at your left.   (4)   lost completely.

10.   One way of magnetizing a piece of steel is to rub it in one direction with a magnet. This procedure
  (1)   lines up the molecules of the steel.
  (2)   makes a compass of the piece of steel.
  (3)   causes the steel eventually to repel the magnet.
  (4)   none of the above

C-3

Scientific terms: acceleration, velocity

[Physicists distinguish between velocity and speed. Velocity includes the direction of travel as well as the rate. To say that a car traveling at a speed of 30 miles per hour has a velocity of 30 miles per hour, we must state the direction in which the car is traveling—for example, due north. Then, we can say that the car has a velocity of 30 miles per hour due north. Thus, velocity is speed, or rate of motion, in a specified direction.

Velocity may be constant, as the velocity of a car that travels with unchanging speed in a given direction. Also, velocity may increase or decrease, as when a car speeds up or slows down. The increase (or decrease) in velocity per unit of time is called *acceleration*. For example, if a car travels two miles faster each second than it traveled the previous second, we say the car has an acceleration of two miles per second each second, or, as a physicist would say it, its acceleration is two miles per second per second.]

Imagine a speedometer attached to a freely falling object in such a way that we can read the velocity at the end of every second. The speedometer tells us that the velocity increases by 32 feet per second every second.

This acceleration, which is due to the force of gravity, is 32 feet per second each second. This value is usually represented by the letter g. In general, if the velocity of an object starting from rest increases a feet per second each second for t seconds, its final velocity is

$$v_{final} = at, \text{ or final velocity}$$
$$\text{equals acceleration}$$
$$\text{multiplied by time.}$$

At the end of 10 seconds the final velocity of a freely falling object is

$$v_{final} = gt = 32 \times 10 = 320 \text{ feet per second.}$$

To find the distance traveled by a freely falling object, we first find the average velocity of the object. Suppose the object falls for 6 seconds. Its final velocity is 32×6, or 192 feet per second. What was the average velocity? The initial velocity was zero. The average velocity must have been one half of 192, or 96 feet per second. The distance the object has fallen is the average velocity times the time during which it was falling, or $96 \times 6 = 576$ feet. Now we have three equations for freely falling bodies:

1. $v_{final} = gt$

2. $v_{average} = \dfrac{1}{2} v_{final}$

3. Distance $s = v_{average} \times t.$

By combining these equations we can obtain a fourth equation:

$$4. \quad s = \frac{1}{2}gt^2, \text{ or } \text{distance equals one-half the product of the acceleration of gravity and time.}$$

Equation 4 makes it possible to find the distance the object has fallen without having to find the average velocity. Applying equation 4 to find the distance a freely falling object has fallen in six seconds, we have:

$$s = \frac{1}{2}gt^2$$
$$s = \frac{1}{2} \times 32 \times 6^2$$
$$s = 16 \times 36$$
$$s = 576 \text{ feet,}$$

which is the same answer we found above.

By means of these equations we can solve any problem of uniformly accelerated motion that starts from rest.

Scientific terms defined

acceleration   The rate of change of velocity.

velocity   Distance traveled in a unit of time in a specified direction, as 85 miles per hour northeast.

11. 1   2   3   4

11.   When a freely falling object, which starts from rest, falls for 8 seconds,
  (1)   its initial velocity is zero.
  (2)   the distance traveled is 1024 feet.
  (3)   the acceleration at the end of the fourth second is 32 feet per second per second.
  (4)   all of the above

12. 1   2   3   4

12.   The change in velocity of an object divided by the time during which this change takes place, is called the
  (1)   final velocity.
  (2)   rate of motion in a particular direction.
  (3)   acceleration.
  (4)   average velocity.

13. 1   2   3   4

13.   A car traveling 42 miles per hour speeds up to 84 miles per hour in 6 seconds. The car's acceleration was
  (1)   8 miles per hour per second.
  (2)   4 miles per hour per second.
  (3)   12 miles per hour per second.
  (4)   7 miles per hour per second.

14. The acceleration of gravity close to the moon's surface is approximately 5 feet per second per second. If an instrument fell out of a space ship 360 feet above the moon's surface, it would fall, before striking the moon, for

14. 1 2 3 4

    (1)   52 seconds.   (3)   144 seconds.
    (2)   12 seconds.   (4)   324 seconds.

    (*Hint:* Use formula 4 in the fifth paragraph of the passage.)

15. The speed of a car traveling 84 miles per hour is cut in half. The car's new velocity is

15. 1 2 3 4

    (1)   21 miles per hour.   (3)   52 miles per hour.
    (2)   42 miles per hour.   (4)   none of the above

C-4

Scientific terms: density, mass, metric system

We say that mercury is "heavier than water," but certainly a gallon of water weighs more than a thimbleful of mercury. It is more accurate to say that mercury is "denser," or has greater density, than water.

[What is density? Let us illustrate the idea of density by means of a softball and an iron ball that is used in the shotput of track and field events. Both balls are about the same size, which means that they have about the same volume, but the iron ball weighs more than 20 times as much as the softball. This means that the weight of every unit of volume of the iron ball is more than 20 times greater than the weight of every unit of volume of the softball. Weight per unit of volume is called *density*. Thus, the iron ball has a greater density than the softball.]

. . . Wood floats on water because it is less dense than water. Iron floats on mercury because the density of iron is less than the density of mercury. But gold, being denser than mercury, will sink in it. The density of anything is its mass [or weight] per unit of volume.

$$\text{density} = \frac{\text{mass}}{\text{volume}}, \text{ or } \left[\frac{\text{weight}}{\text{volume}} \right]$$

Since [on or near the earth's surface] the mass and the weight of an object are numerically the same, we can determine the density of an object by dividing its weight by its volume. In the metric system, density is usually expressed in grams per cubic centimeter; in the English system, in pounds per cubic foot. If 2 cubic feet of granite weigh 300 pounds, then, [using the formula for density, we have

$$\text{density} = \frac{300}{2} = \frac{150 \text{ lbs}}{1 \text{ cu ft}}.$$

The 1 has been left in the denominator of the answer to emphasize that density is weight per *unit of volume*.]

If an object has a regular form, like a cube or a cylinder, we can measure it and calculate its volume. We can find its weight on a balance. Dividing its weight by its volume then gives us its density.

EXAMPLE: A cube of steel measures 2 centimeters along each edge and weighs 64 grams. What is its density?

SOLUTION: The volume of the cube is $2 \times 2 \times 2 = 8$ cubic centimeters. Its density $= 64 \div 8 = 8$ grams per cubic centimeter.

A cube of water 1 foot along each edge has a volume of 1 cubic foot. It weighs 62.4 pounds. Its density is therefore 62.4 pounds per cubic foot.

In the metric system 1 cubic centimeter of water weighs 1 gram. Its density is therefore 1 gram per cubic centimeter.

Scientific terms defined

density   Mass, or weight, per unit of volume.

mass   The amount of matter in a body; also, a measure of the resistance of a body to being accelerated or decelerated, which resistance is proportional to the density of a body.

metric system   Decimal system of measurement in which the meter is the basic unit of length; the kilogram, of mass; and the liter, of volume.

16. A quantity of water having a volume of 5 cubic feet
    (1)   weighs 312 pounds.
    (2)   has a density of 1 gram per cubic centimeter.
    (3)   has a density of 62.4 lbs per cubic foot.
    (4)   all of the above

17. Ice floats on water. From this fact, you can deduce that
    (1)   ice is denser than water.
    (2)   water is denser than ice.
    (3)   ice is less dense than water.
    (4)   both (2) and (3) of the above

18. If a rectangular block of a certain alloy measures 3 centimeters long, 4 centimeters wide, and 5 centimeters high, and its weight is 324 grams, the density of the block is
    (1)   3240 grams per cubic meter.
    (2)   5.4 grams per cubic inch.
    (3)   54 grams per cubic centimeter.
    (4)   none of the above

19. It is more precise to say that lead is denser than beeswax than to say that lead is heavier than beeswax, because
    (1)   any amount of lead is denser than any amount of beeswax.
    (2)   any amount of lead is not necessarily heavier than any amount of beeswax.
    (3)   "denser" is a more precise term than "heavier."
    (4)   both (1) and (2) of the above

20. Four ounces of oak wood occupy the same volume as one ounce of cork. From this fact you can deduce that
    (1)   the wood is denser.
    (2)   equal weights of cork and wood occupy equal volumes.
    (3)   both wood and cork float on water.
    (4)   none of the above

C-5

Scientific terms: calorie, conductometer, convection, insulator, thermal conductivity

Since heat cannot be transferred through a solid, such as an aluminum frying pan, by convection, then it must be passed on from one molecule to the next through the body. When the pan is set on a gas stove, the rapid vibration of the molecules in the flame agitates greater vibration of the aluminum molecules, which in turn pass the energy on through the pan. This method of heat transference is called **conduction.**

We know from experience that some solids conduct heat much better than others. The handle of a silver teaspoon, left in a cup of hot tea, soon becomes hot, whereas we can hold a burning match until the flame almost reaches our fingers. Thus, silver must be a good conductor and wood a very poor one.

Perhaps your chair is constructed of both wood and iron. If so, first feel the wood with your fingers, then feel the iron. Although they must both be at the same temperature, the iron feels cooler. This is because iron is a much better conductor than wood and conducts heat away from the fingers more rapidly, thus making them feel cool.

An interesting experiment can be performed with a "crow's foot" composed of rods of different kinds of metal. This device is known as a *conductometer*. With drops of melted paraffin, matchsticks are stuck to the metal rods equidistant from the junction. The junction is then heated with a gentle flame, and the order in which the sticks melt off indicates the relative conductivities of the metals. . . .

In general, metals are the best solid conductors. The poorest conductor among the common metals is mercury, which is liquid at ordinary temperatures. The best heat conductor known is silver. **Thermal conductivity** is measured in terms of the number of calories transmitted per second through a plate 1 centimeter thick, across an area of 1 square centimeter, when the temperature difference is 1 centigrade degree. For example, the table below shows that approximately half a calorie of heat per second will be transmitted through a square centimeter of aluminum 1 centimeter thick when the temperature difference between the surfaces is 1 centigrade degree. The thermal conductivities of solids range from very good to extremely poor. Extremely poor conductors make good *insulators*.

Thermal Conductivities of Substances

Substance	Thermal Conductivity
Aluminum	0.480
Copper (pure)	0.918

Substance	Thermal Conductivity
German silver	0.07
Iron (pure)	0.161
(steel)	0.115
Mercury	0.0197
Silver (pure)	1.006
Brick (common red)	0.0015
Concrete	0.0022
Glass (window)	0.002
Ice	0.005
Paper	0.0003
Silk	0.000095
Ethyl alcohol	0.000423
Water	0.00131
Air	0.0000568
Nitrogen	0.0000524

Scientific terms defined

calorie A measure of heat; the quantity of heat required to raise the temperature of 1 gram of water 1 degree centigrade; also called the small, or gram, calorie.

conductometer A device for comparing the rates at which different metals transmit heat.

convection The transfer of heat by circulating currents in liquids and gases.

insulator A very poor conductor of heat (or of electricity).

thermal conductivity A measure of the amount of heat transferred through measured amounts of substances in a measured amount of time.

21. One test for distinguishing a genuine diamond from a glass imitation is to touch the back of the hand with the gem in question. A genuine diamond feels cooler than a glass imitation. This test is based on the fact that
    (1) diamond does not take up or lose as much heat as glass.
    (2) diamond conducts heat better than glass.
    (3) glass conducts heat better than diamond.
    (4) all of the above

    21. 1   2   3   4

22. Basing your answer on the thermal conductivities of the substances given in the table, the best substance to use for the handle of a frying pan is
    (1) iron.   (3) silk.
    (2) glass.   (4) paper.

    22. 1   2   3   4

23. 1 2 3 4

23. Suppose you had a conductometer that had one rod made of pure silver and one made of German silver. Suppose, also, that the matchstick falls off the pure silver rod 20 seconds after you begin to heat the apparatus. The matchstick should fall off the German silver rod in approximately
    (1) 4 minutes, 40 seconds.   (3) 3 minutes, 40 seconds.
    (2) 4 minutes, 66 seconds.   (4) 2 minutes, 40 seconds.

24. 1 2 3 4

24. If the rods on a conductometer are made of iron, copper, German silver, and aluminum the order in which the matchsticks will fall is
    (1) German silver, iron, copper, aluminum.
    (2) aluminum, copper, iron, German silver.
    (3) copper, aluminum, iron, German silver.
    (4) copper, German silver, aluminum, iron.

25. 1 2 3 4

25. If you made a double-walled container for the purpose of keeping food cold, it would be best to fill the space between the walls with
    (1) paper.   (3) ethyl alcohol.
    (2) silk.   (4) air.

ANSWERS AND EXPLANATIONS

1. **(4)** If light streamed from a viewer's eyes, he would never be in the dark; his eyes would act as natural flashlights. Hence, (1) and (2) are correct. Paragraph one of the passage states that light streams out of the eyes much like water. Thus, (3) is true. With (1), (2), and (3) all true, (4) is the correct answer.

2. **(3)** Paragraph four notes that Newton considered light to be emitted from a source ("luminous body") and paragraph six mentions Huygens' waves as coming "from a source." Thus, (3) is the correct answer. Only Newton believed light to be composed of corpuscles, hence Newton and Huygens could not have held this idea in common. Thus, (1) is not correct. Paragraph three states that light does not bend around a corner. Thus, (2) is not correct. The difference between the Greeks' idea of light streaming from the viewer's eyes and Newton's and Huygens' idea of light being emitted by a source is explained in the passage. Thus, (4) is incorrect.

3. **(2)** In the next-to-the-last paragraph, Huygens explains that "if waves are large and the obstacle is small, the waves will bend around the obstacle and be seen on the other side." This is the situation described in (2), and thus (2) is the correct answer. To say that an obstruction is too small to be seen is not an explanation; it repeats the question in different words. Thus, (1) is not correct. If an object absorbed light rays, it would prevent those rays from reaching the eye and would stand out amid the light as a darker space; that is, a shadow. This is the opposite of what Huygens claimed for a very small object. Thus, (3) is not correct.

4. **(4)** If the light moved from the viewer's eyes toward both the object and the fire, the object would be seen in its natural colors (3), and not as a dark shape against the fire (1). Thus, with (1) and (3) true, the correct answer is (4). The object between the viewer and a fire might be hard to distinguish, but with light streaming upon it from the viewer's eyes, there is no reason to believe, according to the Greeks' theory, that it would not be seen.

5. **(3)** Nothing in the passage states or implies that the theories of Newton and Huygens have been proved false. The last paragraph states that modern physics accepts both theories. The particular Greek theory described above has, of course, been proved false by modern knowledge of the reflection of light. Thus, (1) and (2) are not correct. The Greeks considered light as streaming from a viewer's eyes; hence, the light was in motion. Newton's corpuscles were emitted (sent forth) from luminous objects; hence, the corpuscles were in motion. Huygens' light waves, too, were in motion. Thus, light in all three theories was a kind of motion, making (3) the correct answer.

6. **(2)** The opening sentence of the passage directly provides the answer given in (2), which, then, is the correct answer. Since (2) is correct, (1) must

be incorrect. The first paragraph says that Greek mariners used bits of lodestone as crude compasses, but neither they nor anyone else *invented* magnetism, which is a natural phenomenon. Hence, (3) is incorrect. The first paragraph also says that magicians of ancient times used magnetism, but it was not their product for the same reason it was not an invention of Greek sailors. Thus, (4) is incorrect.

7. **(4)** Choices (1), (2), and (3) restate in different words the Law of Magnetic Poles: like magnetic poles repel; unlike poles attract. Thus, the first three choices are true, and (4) is the correct answer.

8. **(4)** The fourth paragraph states directly that the north pole of a magnet is a north-seeking pole. Hence, (1) is true. Since a north-seeking pole is a north pole, the north pole of a compass will, according to the Law of Magnetic Poles, repel the north pole of a magnet. Thus, (2) is correct. When we say that the north pole of a magnet seeks the earth's north magnetic pole, we are saying that the earth's pole attracts the magnet's pole. Conversely, the Law of Magnetic Poles enables us to deduce that the earth's south magnetic pole must repel the north pole of a magnet. If this statement seems to contradict the Law of Magnetic Poles, note that the earth's north magnetic pole acts like a south pole since it attracts a magnet's north pole. Hence, the earth's south magnetic pole acts like a north pole and repels a magnet's north pole. Thus, (3) is true. With (1), (2), and (3) being correct, (4) is the correct answer.

9. **(2)** The last paragraph says that when a magnet is cut in half, the poles of two new magnets that are formed have their poles oriented in the same directions as the poles of the original magnet. Therefore, the new magnets would have their north poles at your left. Thus, (2) is the correct answer.

10. **(1)** The last paragraph explains that magnetized metal has its molecules lined up so that their north poles point in one direction and their south poles in the opposite direction. Thus, (1) is the correct answer. The process of magnetizing the piece of steel does not in itself make a compass of it, although the magnetized steel can be used as a compass. Thus, (2) is not correct. We cannot say that the magnetized piece of steel will repel the magnet. Although the piece of steel becomes a magnet, repulsion will take place only if like poles of the two magnets are brought near each other. Thus, (3) is not correct.

11. **(4)** The question states that the freely falling object was at rest before it began to fall; therefore, its velocity was zero. Thus, (1) is true. By using formula 4 in paragraph five, we can find s, the distance traveled by a freely falling object, thus:

$$s = \frac{1}{2} g t^2$$

$$s = \frac{1}{2} \times 32 \times 8^2$$

$$s = 1024 \text{ feet.}$$

Hence, (2) is true. As long as the object is falling freely, its acceleration is 32 feet per second per second, whether at the end of the fourth second or any other time during its fall. Hence, (3) is true. With (1), (2) and (3) true, (4) is the correct answer.

12. (3) Paragraph two explains that acceleration is increase or decrease in velocity per unit of time. Thus, if we divide the change in velocity by the time in which the change was taking place, we obtain the acceleration. Hence, (3) is the correct answer. The question gives "change in velocity" as one of the quantities entering into the problem. If the question had said simply "velocity," then dividing velocity by time would have given "average velocity," choice (4), and is incorrect.

13. (4) The increase in speed is 42 miles per hour $(84 - 42 = 42)$. Since acceleration is increase per unit of time, you must divide the 42-mile-per-hour increase by the length of time (6 seconds) in which the increase took place. Then, $42 \div 6 = 7$ miles per hour per second. Thus, (4) is the correct answer.

14. (2) The question gives you distance (360 feet) and acceleration (5 feet per second per second) and asks you to find the time. All of these quantities appear in formula 4 of paragraph five.

$$s = \frac{1}{2} gt^2$$

$$2s = gt^2$$

$$\frac{2s}{g} = t^2$$

$$t^2 = \frac{2s}{g}$$

$$t = \sqrt{\frac{2 \times 360}{5}}$$

$$t = \sqrt{144}$$

$$t = 12 \text{ seconds}$$

Thus, (2) is the correct answer.

15. (4) Paragraph one states that velocity is speed in a specified direction. Since the direction of the car is not given in the question, it is incorrect to speak of the car's velocity. Thus, neither (1), (2), nor (3) can be correct, and (4) is the correct answer.

16. (4) The next-to-the-last paragraph states that 1 cubic foot of water weighs 62.4 pounds; therefore, five cubic feet of water weigh 5×62.4 pounds, or 312 pounds. Thus, (1) is true. The last paragraph states that water has a density of 1 gram per cubic centimeter. Hence, (2) is correct. If 1 cubic foot of water weighs 62.4 pounds, then water must have a density of 62.4 lbs per cubic foot, a fact stated in the next-to-the-last paragraph. Thus, (3) is true. With (1), (2), and (3) all being true, (4) is the correct answer.

17. (4) Paragraph three states that wood floats on water because it is less dense than water; also, that iron floats on mercury because iron is less dense than mercury. From these facts, you can deduce that a material that floats is less dense than the material it floats on. Therefore, since ice floats on water, ice must be less dense than water (3), which is the same as saying that water is denser than ice (2). With (2) and (3) true, choice (4) is the correct answer.

18. (4) A block with the dimensions 3 cm × 4 cm × 5 cm has a volume of 60 cubic centimeters. If we want to find its density, we want to know how much of the weight (or mass) of the block will be found in each cubic centimeter. So we divide the weight in grams by the number of cubic centimeters. Here, we divide 324 grams by 60 cubic centimeters, getting 5.4, or 5.4 grams per cubic centimeter. Hence, (1) is far from being the correct answer; (2) is numerically correct, but gives the answer in grams per *cubic inch*, instead of per cubic centimeter; and (3) is in the right units of measurement, but is numerically wrong. Thus, with choices (1), (2), and (3) wrong, (4) is the correct answer.

19. (4) The density of lead is 11.3 grams per cubic centimeter and the density of beeswax is 0.965 grams per cubic centimeter. These densities hold true for any amount of lead or any amount of beeswax (1). But you can easily calculate that a dozen cubic centimeters of beeswax weighs more than one cubic centimeter of lead. Therefore, *any* amount of lead is not necessarily heavier than any amount of beeswax (2). With (1) and (2) true, (4) is the correct answer. We cannot say that "denser" is a more precise term than "heavier" unless we first know the situation in which we use the term. The answers to (1) and (2) show that "denser" is more precise in (1) and "heavier" more precise in (2).

20. (1) The question says that four ounces of oak wood occupy the same volume as one ounce of cork. If we consider this particular volume to be a unit of volume, then there is four times as much weight of oak wood as of cork in this volume. Since density is weight per unit volume, oak wood, which has four times as much weight per unit of volume, is four times as dense as cork. Thus, (1) is the correct answer. In the answer to (1), we determined that four times as much weight of oak wood as of cork occupy equal volumes; therefore, it cannot also be true that equal weights of the two materials occupy equal volumes. Thus, (2) is not correct. Although it is true that both wood and cork float on water, this fact cannot be deduced from the facts given in the first sentence of the question. Thus, (3) is incorrect.

21. (2) Paragraph three explains that iron feels cooler than wood, when both are at the same temperature, because iron—a better conductor—conducts heat away from your fingers more rapidly. From this, you can reason that diamond feels cooler than glass because diamond conducts heat from the back of the hand more rapidly. Thus, (2) is the correct answer. Although diamond takes up heat more rapidly than glass, diamond and glass both being in the same place for several

minutes would eventually be at the same temperature—both taking up or losing heat to reach equal temperatures. Thus, (1) is not correct.

22. **(3)** The last sentence of the passage states, "extremely poor conductors are good *insulators*." The poorest conductor of the four choices—the substance with the lowest thermal conductivity (according to the table)—is silk. Therefore, silk would make the best insulator against heat in the handle of a frying pan.

23. **(1)** According to the table, pure silver has a thermal conductivity approximately 14 times as great as German silver ($1.006 \div 0.07 = 14.4$). If it takes 20 seconds for heat to be conducted through the pure silver rod, it will take 14 times as long for heat to pass through the German silver rod. Then, 14×20 seconds $= 280$ seconds, and 280 seconds are 4 minutes, 40 seconds. Thus, (1) is the correct answer.

24. **(3)** The greater the conductivity of a rod, the sooner the heat will reach the paraffin, melt it, and cause the matchstick to fall. The table shows that, in descending order, the conductivities of the metals listed in the question are copper (0.918), aluminum (0.480), iron (0.161), and German silver (0.07). Thus, (3) is the correct answer.

25. **(4)** According to the table, the poorest conductor—and therefore the best insulator—among those listed in the question is air. So, air between the walls of the container would do the best job of keeping heat from the food. Thus, (4) is the correct answer.

EARTH SCIENCE

DIRECTIONS: Read each of the following passages. Choose the BEST answer to each question. Then blacken the space under that number in the answer column. You may go back to the passage as often as necessary to answer the questions.

ANSWERS AND EXPLANATIONS APPEAR AT THE END OF THE CHAPTER

D-1

Scientific terms: fault, landslip, lithosphere, magma, tectonic earthquake, tsunami, volcanic earthquake

Most earthquakes are the result of movement along an existing fracture in the deep rock beds. The walls of a fault are usually very closely pressed together. Rock beds that are under stress undergo many years of slowly increasing pressures before they move along a fracture. Finally the stress exceeds the strength of the rock. Then a sudden movement occurs along the fault, causing the earthquake vibrations. According to the *elastic rebound theory* of earthquakes, pressure is exerted on two adjacent rock areas from opposite directions for long periods of time. The pressure may be upward, downward, or sideways. As it increases, the rocks bend slowly. Eventually the strain becomes so great that the rocks split apart, either vertically or horizontally, along the fault line.

The San Andreas fault, along which the California earthquake occurred in 1906, can be traced over a distance of 270 miles. The chief movement along the fault was horizontal. The southwest side shifted toward the north in relation to the opposite side. In some places the horizontal displacement was 21 feet. . . .

There are thousands of known faults all over the earth. Few of them, however, seem to be the sources of earthquakes. Most earthquakes, therefore, must probably have their source in faults below the earth's surface. The trembling of the solid rock immediately after faulting sets up the earthquake shocks. These may be strong enough to affect an entire continent or may be so slight that sensitive instruments are needed to record their presence.

Earthquakes that are the result of crustal movements, such as faulting, are classed as *tectonic earthquakes*. These larger quakes usually originate in the outer 20 to 100 miles of the lithosphere. Earthquakes are also often associated with volcanic activity. *Volcanic earthquakes* are due either to explosive volcanic activity or to the flow of magma below the crust. Sometimes tectonic earthquakes may trigger volcanic

82

eruption. Earthquakes caused by volcanic activity are always relatively feeble compared with the more violent, tectonic earthquakes. They may, however, be the cause of greater local damage.

Landslides occurring over a wide area may result in earthquakes of lesser intensity than those associated with faulting or volcanism. *Landslips,* as such landslides are called, usually occur in regions of rugged relief. They sometimes also take place on the sea floor near the margins of the submerged continental shelves.

Earthquakes of tectonic, volcanic, or landslip origin may also occur under the ocean. Their most noticeable effect is the production of seismic sea waves, or *tsunamis* (tsoo-*nah*-meez).

Scientific terms defined

fault   A fracture in a rock surface, along which there is movement of the two sides of the fracture in relation to each other.

landslip   A landslide.

lithosphere   The solid, outer part of the earth composed of rock.

magma   Molten or semimolten rock materials below the earth's surface.

tectonic earthquake   An earthquake that is the result of movements of the earth's crust along a fault.

tsunami   Scientific name for a tidal wave; also, a seismic sea wave.

volcanic earthquake   An earthquake due to the explosive activity of a volcano or the flow of magma beneath the crust.

1. The most violent earthquakes are caused by
   (1) movements along faults.   (3) volcanoes.
   (2) landslips.   (4) all of the above

2. In tough rock, as compared to brittle rock, the time between earthquakes will probably be
   (1) shorter.   (3) about the same.
   (2) longer.   (4) none of the above

3. One force that builds mountains is the folding of the earth's crust. Earthquakes are most likely to be found in
   (1) newly formed mountains.   (3) middle-aged mountains.
   (2) old, worn-down mountains.   (4) plains.

4. The earth's crust is between 7 and 20 miles thick. Large earthquakes take place
   (1) only in the crust.   (3) both in the crust and below it.
   (2) only below the crust.   (4) above the crust.

5. A tectonic earthquake may be the cause of a
   (1) volcanic earthquake.   (3) tsunami.
   (2) landslip earthquake.   (4) all of the above

1. 1 2 3 4

2. 1 2 3 4

3. 1 2 3 4

4. 1 2 3 4

5. 1 2 3 4

D-2

Scientific terms: atmosphere, compound, element, hydrosphere, lithosphere, water vapor

We are accustomed to believing that we are living on the surface of our planet. Seldom do we think of ourselves as creatures compelled to live within the limits of a vast sea of gases, as a fish is compelled to live in water. Nevertheless, man is adapted to live at the bottom of the earth's atmosphere. This envelope of gases, at least a thousand miles thick, surrounds the entire planet. What we are used to thinking of as the surface of the earth is only the surface of the lithosphere or hydrosphere. There is no true "surface" because the upper edge of the atmosphere blends gradually into outer space. Most of the life on earth exists in the relatively narrow region where the atmosphere joins the lithosphere and hydrosphere. . . .

The bulk of the atmosphere is a mixture of two gases, oxygen and nitrogen. Of these, nitrogen is the more abundant. It accounts for 78 percent of the total volume of the air while oxygen makes up 21 percent. The remaining 1 percent is mostly argon and carbon dioxide. Table 1 shows the normal composition of the atmosphere near sea level.

The gases listed are always present in approximately the same amounts. However, there are other substances which may be found in widely varying amounts. The most important is water vapor. At times this compound may make up 5 percent or more of the total volume of the air. The substances that are usually present in much smaller proportions in the atmosphere are listed in Table 2.

The composition of the atmosphere is almost constant. However, [small amounts of] the principal gases, nitrogen and oxygen, are being continuously lost into space or combined with other elements or compounds on the earth. If there were no means of replacement, the supply of oxygen in the atmosphere would be exhausted in about 3000 years. The nitrogen supply would be lost in 100 million years. [The lost gases are replenished by certain processes that involve living things. For example, plants in the process of photosynthesis (the formation of starches from carbon dioxide and water in the presence of sunlight) excrete oxygen into the air.]

Table 1

Gases in Pure Dry Air

Gas	Symbol or Formula	Percent (by volume)
nitrogen	N_2	78.084
oxygen	O_2	20.946
argon	Ar	.934
carbon dioxide	CO_2	.033
neon	Ne	.001818
helium	He	.000524
methane	CH_4	.0002
krypton	Kr	.000114
hydrogen	H_2	.00005
nitrous oxide	N_2O	.00005
xenon	Xe	.0000087

Table 2

Variable Substances in Air

Substance	Symbol or Formula
water vapor	H_2O
ozone	O_3
ammonia	NH_3
hydrogen sulfide	H_2S
sulfur dioxide	SO_2
sulfur trioxide	SO_3
carbon monoxide	CO
radon	Ra
dust (soot, rock, sea salt)	

Scientific terms defined

atmosphere The earth's envelope of gases.

compound A homogeneous substance made up of two or more chemical elements combined in fixed and invariable proportion by weight.

element A substance that cannot be decomposed into simpler substances by chemical means.

hydrosphere The earth's envelope of water.

lithosphere The solid part of the earth.

water vapor Water in a gaseous state.

6.   1   2   3   4

6. The uppermost part of the earth's surface
   (1) is at least 1000 miles above the ground.
   (2) blends gradually into interplanetary space.
   (3) does not provide the earth with a true outer surface.
   (4) all of the above

7.   1   2   3   4

7. Fish live in the hydrosphere and human beings live in the atmosphere, but both are dependent on the atmosphere because both
   (1) need oxygen.
   (2) use carbon dioxide in the process of converting stored food into energy.
   (3) drink water in which air is dissolved.
   (4) none of the above

8.   1   2   3   4

8. A comparison of the rates at which nitrogen and oxygen are being lost to outer space shows that the rate of loss of nitrogen is
   (1) faster.   (3) about the same.
   (2) slower.   (4) variable.

9.   1   2   3   4

9. Of the substances listed in Table 2, the one most likely to influence the weather is
   (1) carbon monoxide.   (3) sulfur dioxide.
   (2) hydrogen sulfide.   (4) water vapor.

10.   1   2   3   4

10. In the process of photosynthesis, green plants are continually putting oxygen into the air, yet the amount of this gas remains constant because
    (1) animals breathe the excess oxygen, changing it to carbon dioxide.
    (2) the earth is continually losing oxygen to outer space.
    (3) the burning of wood, coal, and other carbon compounds uses up great amounts of oxygen.
    (4) all of the above

D-3

Scientific terms: friction, inertia, lava, satellite

Sir George Darwin, son of the great naturalist, Charles Darwin, formulated a theory to explain the fact that our moon always turns the same side to the earth, so that we can see only one half of our satellite's surface. Darwin wondered whether the fact that the moon's period of rotation equals the time of its revolution around the earth is due to chance or the working of natural law.

Darwin answered the question with the following argument. The gravitational pull of the moon causes tides on earth. Since most of the earth's surface is covered by water, tidal crests can form on two opposite points of the earth. A line connecting the crests is directed toward the moon. The earth's rotation beneath the tidal crests causes two great waves to travel around the earth. These waves cause the earth's high tides. The tidal waves are fed continually by water from areas of low tide. This causes a current to run contrary to the line of the earth's rotation, thereby creating appreciable friction because water naturally resists any displacement of its particles. This tidal friction acts as a brake on the earth's rotation, gradually slowing it down. This continual, nearly imperceptible braking process will last until the tidal waves cease their movement and the tides and their resultant friction come to an end. This will happen when the earth's rotation has become so slow that one earth day equals the moon's period of revolution around the earth—in other words, when the earth keeps the same side turned to the moon so that the moon no longer revolves around the earth.

The fact that we always see the same side of the moon probably originated in the foregoing process. In the very distant past, Darwin surmised, the moon's surface was covered by molten lava. At that time, the moon's rotation was probably much faster than it is now. It gradually slowed down as the earth's gravitational attraction caused ever-increasing tidal movement and consequent friction in the molten lava. This braking effect has long ceased, but the braking effect of the moon on the earth (through the earth's tides) will not cease for many millions of years. Darwin gave three reasons for this series of events. First, because the moon is much smaller than the earth, the resistance of the moon's inertia to the braking influence of the earth was weak. Second, the earth exerted a much greater tidal influence on the moon than the moon on the earth. Third, the moon's tidal movement took place in lava, matter which was viscous rather than completely liquid, as the earth's waters are, and whose inner friction was greater than the earth's freely moving oceans.

Scientific terms defined

friction Resistance to the rolling, sliding, or flowing motion of one body moving relative to another with which it is in contact.

inertia Resistance offered by a body to a change of its state of rest or motion.

lava Molten rock material that flows through volcanoes and fissures onto the surface of the earth from sources below.

satellite Any celestial body that revolves around a larger body; a natural or artificial moon.

11. The braking effect exerted by the moon on the earth
  (1) still causes molten tides on the moon.
  (2) works through the effect of the ocean tides which the moon causes.
  (3) will continue for millions of years.
  (4) both (2) and (3) of the above

12. If the earth had no oceans it would
  (1) be spinning faster.
  (2) be spinning slower.
  (3) exert a greater braking effect on the moon.
  (4) be stationary.

13. If the moon were to speed up the time of rotation on its axis and still keep one side always facing the earth, the time necessary for the moon to revolve around the earth would be
  (1) longer.   (3) unchanged.
  (2) shorter.   (4) irregular.

14. At one time in its history, the earth was molten. At that time, the earth's rate of rotation was slowed by the moon's gravitational influence
  (1) which caused lava tides and their consequent friction.
  (2) on both lava tides and on the earth's oceans.
  (3) only on the earth's oceans.
  (4) both (2) and (3) of the above

15. Gases are fluid. From this we conclude that the earth's atmosphere, which is a mixture of gases,
  (1) moves around the earth in tides due to the moon's gravitational influence.
  (2) provides a braking force on the earth's rotation.
  (3) is too thin, in comparison with the earth's waters, to provide a braking force on the earth's rotation.
  (4) both (1) and (2) of the above

D-4

Scientific terms: debris, erosion, evaporation, groundwater, hydrologic cycle, infiltration, precipitation, runoff, transpiration

Through millions of years of earth history, agencies of erosion have been working constantly to reduce the land masses to the level of the seas. Of these agencies, running water is the most important. Year after year, the streams of the earth move staggering amounts of debris and dissolved material through their valleys to the great settling basins, the oceans.

"All the rivers run into the sea, yet the sea is not full: unto the place from whence the rivers come, thither they return again," reads Ecclesiastes 1:7. And thither they still return, for in the final analysis the water that runs off the slopes of the land in thin sheets, and then travels on in rills, streams, and rivers, is derived from the oceans. There is one exception: volcanic eruptions apparently bring water to the surface from deep beneath the earth. But once it has reached the surface, this water also follows the general pattern of water movement from sea to land and back again to the sea, a pattern that we call the *hydrologic cycle*.

The Hydrologic Cycle*

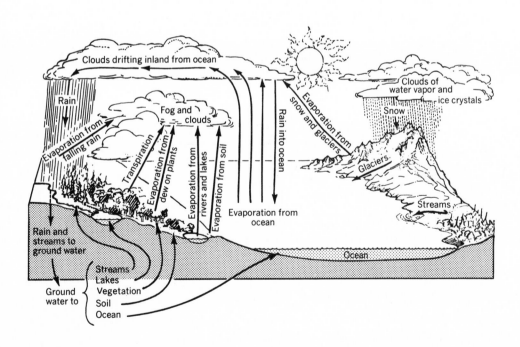

* From *Principles of Geology,* Third Edition, by James Gilluly, Aaron C. Waters, and A. O. Woodford. W. H. Freeman and Company. Copyright © 1968.

Precipitation and Stream Flow

Once water has fallen on the land as precipitation, it follows one of the many paths that make up the hydrologic cycle. By far the greatest part is evaporated back to the air directly, or is taken up by the plants and transpired (breathed back) by them to the atmosphere. A smaller amount follows the path of *runoff,* the water that flows off the land. And the smallest amount of precipitation soaks into the ground through *infiltration.* . . . Bearing in mind the ways in which water that falls as precipitation proceeds through the hydrologic cycle, we can express the amount of runoff by the following generalized formula:

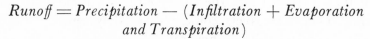

$$Runoff = Precipitation - (Infiltration + Evaporation\ and\ Transpiration)$$

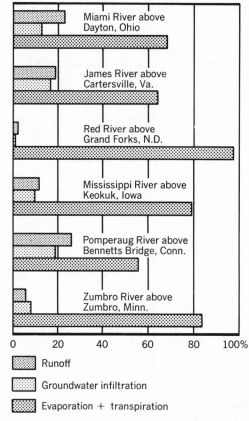

What Happens to Precipitation That Falls in Certain River Basins (Valleys)

Scientific terms defined

debris Unconsolidated material, such as sand, mud, pebbles, rock fragments, and dead and decaying plant and animal material.

erosion The wearing down of the earth's surface by such agents as running water, wind, weathering of rock, glaciers, etc.

evaporation The changing of water to water vapor.

groundwater Water that penetrates into spaces within the rocks of the earth's crust.

hydrologic cycle The continuous process by which water is evaporated from the sea, precipitated over the land, and eventually returned to the sea.

infiltration The soaking of water into the ground and into spaces within the rocks of the earth's crust.

precipitation A deposit on the earth of rain, sleet, snow, hail, or mist.

runoff Water that flows off the land into streams, lakes, and other bodies of water.

transpiration The process by which water escapes from a living plant into the atmosphere.

16. More than half the water that falls on the land
    (1) becomes runoff.
    (2) becomes groundwater.
    (3) goes into the air through evaporation and transpiration.
    (4) becomes ice.

16. 1 2 3 4

17. With one exception, all the water that runs off the land is derived from one source: the oceans. The exception is water that
    (1) comes from melting ice.
    (2) is brought to the surface by volcanic eruptions.
    (3) comes from the decay of dead plants and animals.
    (4) comes from rocks.

17. 1 2 3 4

18. Water that falls to earth as precipitation becomes runoff, except for that which is involved in the processes of
    (1) transpiration.   (3) evaporation.
    (2) infiltration.   (4) all of the above

18. 1 2 3 4

19. Basing your answer on the diagram of the hydrologic cycle, when precipitation falls as snow on mountain tops, the water that makes up the snow
    (1) remains locked in the deep snow of snowfields.
    (2) evaporates from snowfields and glaciers.
    (3) moves down mountains as glaciers and then melts.
    (4) both (2) and (3) of the above

19. 1 2 3 4

20. In order that the hydrologic cycle can operate, one of the following is necessary:
    (1) snow.   (3) wind.
    (2) rain.   (4) groundwater infiltration.

20. 1 2 3 4

D-5

Scientific terms: bedrock, core, crust, mantle, mantle rock, outcrop

Most scientists agree that the earth was a large ball of molten rock [at an early period of its history]. In time, the outer surface of the molten rock cooled to form the earth's solid crust. The lava which comes out of volcanoes and recordings of shock waves from earthquakes and nuclear bomb testing provide us with a great deal of information about the structure and composition of the earth's interior. These studies indicate the existence of three layers, (1) the outer crust, (2) an intermediate zone, the mantle, and (3) the core.

The crust consists of a thin layer of lightweight rock which is approximately 10 to 20 miles deep. The various surface features found on the crust include mountains, volcanoes, plains, plateaus, deep river valleys, deserts, and oceans. The outer surface of the crust on the continents consists mainly of a loose covering of soil, sand, and rock fragments called mantle rock. [Beneath the seas, the surface is covered with mud near the continents and with ooze farther from land.]

Below the outer covering lies a layer of solid rock called bedrock. The bedrock varies in thickness in different parts of the crust from less than one inch to several hundred feet. Bedrock is frequently found on the surface of the earth, especially in mountain regions. An area of exposed bedrock is called an outcrop.

Beneath the earth's crust lies a dense iron- and magnesium-bearing layer of rock called the mantle. This layer, which is about 2,000 miles thick, extends to a point that is almost midway between the crust and the center of the earth. The rock in this intermediate zone is hot [about 4000° F] and almost plastic in nature.

The dense core of the earth lies directly below the mantle and extends 2,000 miles to the earth's center. The rock located in this region [is made up mainly of iron plus a small amount of nickel and cobalt]. The temperature of the core is about 5500° F, higher than the melting points of these metals. The pressure is almost 60 million pounds per square inch. This great pressure is responsible for the fact that the metals in this layer are probably solid.

All the rocks of the earth are composed of minerals which are in turn composed of elements. . . . Of the 92 elements which occur naturally, only eight make up more than 98 percent of the earth's crust. Oxygen and silicon, two nonmetals, are the most abundant elements in the earth's crust. Aluminum, iron, and calcium are the most abundant metallic elements.

Scientific terms defined

bedrock   The unweathered solid rock of the earth's crust.

core   The dense, innermost zone of the earth.

crust   The outer layer of the solid earth.

mantle   The intermediate zone of the earth extending from the lower boundary of the crust to the outer boundary of the core and composed of iron- and magnesium-bearing semiplastic rock.

mantle rock   Layers of loose weathered rock lying on solid bedrock.

outcrop   An exposed part of bedrock.

21. The temperature of the earth's core is high enough to melt the metals of which it is made. However, the core probably is solid because
    (1)   without air, the metals cannot melt.
    (2)   the core is under such great pressure that it remains solid.
    (3)   the combination of nickel, cobalt, and iron form an alloy with a melting point higher than the temperature of the core.
    (4)   none of the above

22. In order from lightest to heaviest, the metals that make up the earth's mantle and core are magnesium, iron, nickel, and cobalt. From this fact you deduce that the reason for the composition of the core is that
    (1)   the heavier metals sank to the center of a once-molten earth.
    (2)   random mixing of elements at the beginning of the earth resulted in the present distribution in the mantle and core.
    (3)   the rotation of the earth, when it was molten, distributed the lighter elements in the core.
    (4)   none of the above

23. In the earth's crust the temperature increases about 80° for every mile of depth. Below the crust, the rate of increase in temperature
    (1)   becomes greater.   (3)   remains constant.
    (2)   becomes less.   (4)   is 90° for every mile.

24. The reason one is likely to find exposed bedrock in mountainous regions is that
    (1)   mountain-building forces push the bedrock to the surface.
    (2)   the process of erosion and the force of gravitation move sand, soil, and any other form of the mantle rock to the lowlands, leaving the bedrock exposed in the higher parts of the earth's surface.
    (3)   both (1) and (2).
    (4)   none of the above

25. Our knowledge of the earth's interior is based on
    (1)   direct observations.   (3)   mathematical calculations.
    (2)   chemical analyses.   (4)   indirect observations.

ANSWERS AND EXPLANATIONS

1. **(1)** Paragraph four explains that earthquakes that result from faulting of the earth's rocks are tectonic earthquakes and that these are more violent than volcanic earthquakes. Paragraph five says that tectonic and volcanic earthquakes are both of greater intensity than those caused by landslips. Thus, (1) is the correct answer.

2. **(2)** Paragraph one explains that one kind of earthquake is caused by pressure building up along a fault until the strain becomes so great that the rock splits apart along the fault. Tough rock, then, would probably stand the strain of increasing pressure longer than brittle rock, which breaks easily. Thus, (2) is the correct answer.

3. **(1)** Folding of the earth's crust causes bending pressure, which could result in the breaking of rock and consequent earthquakes. Therefore, newly formed mountains having recently folded rock would be most likely to have earthquakes. Thus, (1) is the correct answer. The pressure due to folding is much less in middle-aged mountains, and is practically gone in old mountains. Although middle-aged and old mountains do have some earthquakes, they are not the places "most likely" (as the question asks) to have earthquakes.

4. **(3)** Paragraph four says that tectonic earthquakes usually originate in the outer 20 to 100 miles of the lithosphere. If the crust is only 20 miles thick, tectonic earthquakes must take place both in the crust and below it. Thus, (3) is the correct answer. Volcanic earthquakes take place very close to the surface and landslip earthquakes take place on the surface. However, neither of these types is a large earthquake, therefore (1), (2), and (4) cannot be correct.

5. **(4)** Paragraph four says that a tectonic earthquake may trigger a volcanic eruption, and therefore may be the cause of a volcanic earthquake. Thus, (1) is true. An intense earthquake, such as a tectonic one, can shake loose a mass of earth, mud, or loose rock, thereby causing a landslip. Hence, (2) is true. The last paragraph states that earthquakes may produce tsunamis. Thus, (3) is true. With choices (1), (2), and (3) all true, (4) is the correct answer.

6. **(4)** The first paragraph explains that the outer part of the atmosphere should be considered the earth's surface, but, since the atmosphere—which is at least 1000 miles thick—blends into outer space, the earth has no true (outer) surface. Thus, (1), (2), and (3) are correct, making (4) the correct answer.

7. **(1)** Both human beings and fish are animals, and as such both need oxygen for use in the process of converting stored food to energy. Thus, (1) is the correct answer and (2) is incorrect. Although both human beings and fish may drink water in which air is dissolved, such an action is not necessary; it is not the manner in which either fish or human beings obtain air (oxygen) for use in their bodies. Thus, (3) is incorrect.

8. (2) The last paragraph says that at the present rate of loss and with no replenishment, the supply of oxygen in the atmosphere would be exhausted in 3000 years. There is approximately four times as much nitrogen as oxygen in the atmosphere. If the loss of nitrogen was at the same rate as the loss of oxygen, the nitrogen would be exhausted in 4 times 3000 years, or 120,000 years. However, the passage says that it would take 100 million years to lose all the nitrogen. Therefore, nitrogen is being lost at a much slower rate than oxygen is. Hence, (2) is the correct answer.

9. (4) According to paragraph three, water vapor may make up as much as five percent of the atmosphere by volume. Clouds are formed of water droplets that have condensed from water vapor. Raindrops, snowflakes, hailstones, and sleet are products of condensed water vapor. Humidity varies with the amount of water vapor in the air. All these things are important causes or effects of weather. Thus, (4) is the correct answer.

10. (4) Animals, by breathing air, take out oxygen in the process of respiration that changes the oxygen to carbon dioxide. Hence, (1) is true. The last paragraph states that the earth is continually losing oxygen to outer space and that this loss is being restored by green plants in the process of photosynthesis. We can look at this series of events from another viewpoint and say that the loss of oxygen to space prevents an increase in oxygen in the atmosphere. Thus, (2) is true. The burning of wood, coal, and other carbon compounds is a well-known process in which oxygen is used. Hence, (3) is true. With (1), (2), and (3) true, (4) is the correct answer.

11. (4) Paragraph two states that tidal friction acts as a brake on the earth's rotation, slowing it down (2), and paragraph three says that the braking effect of the moon on the earth will not cease for many millions of years (3). With (2) and (3) true, (4) is the correct answer.

12. (1) Since it is the earth's tides that exert a braking effect on the earth's rotation, without those tides the earth would be spinning faster. Thus, (1) is the correct answer. The second paragraph explains how the moon, acting upon the earth's tides, slows the earth's rotation. In acting on the earth's tides, the moon is performing work, which takes energy. The energy used up by the moon in this manner slows the rotation of the moon. Thus, (3) is not correct. Choice (4) is scientifically untenable.

13. (2) At present, the time for one revolution of the moon around the earth equals the time for one rotation of the moon on its axis. If this relationship is to continue for a moon that rotates on its axis in less time, then the moon will have to revolve around the earth in less time; that is, its time of revolution would be shorter. Thus, (2) is the correct answer.

14. (1) Paragraph three explains how the earth caused lava tides on a molten moon; therefore, the moon would cause lava tides on a molten earth, slowing the earth down. Thus, (1) is the correct answer. A molten

earth was too hot to have any water on its surface, so it had no oceans. Hence, (2) and (3) are not correct.

15. **(4)** The second paragraph explains how the earth's oceans, under the influence of the moon's gravitational attraction, act as a brake on the earth's rotation. The earth's atmosphere, too, is under the influence of the moon. From this, we can reason that there are tides in the atmosphere, choice (1), and that they, too, are acting as a brake on the earth's rotation, choice (2). With both (1) and (2) true, (4) is the correct answer. Although air is much thinner (less dense) than water, air is matter, and its particles, like those of water, resist displacement, thereby causing friction. This friction, acting on the earth's surface, provides a braking force which is much less than that caused by the oceans, but is still a braking force. Thus, choice (3) is not correct.

16. **(3)** Paragraph three states directly that by far most precipitation is evaporated back into the atmosphere directly or indirectly through transpiration by plants. The bar graphs for every river basin charted indicate that evaporation and transpiration account for more than 50% of precipitation. Thus, (3) is the correct answer. The bar graphs contradict answers (1) and (2). Precipitation will not become ice, of course, unless it falls in the colder parts of the earth's atmosphere. Thus, (4) is incorrect.

17. **(2)** Paragraph two states directly that the one exception to water being derived from the oceans is the water brought to the surface from deep in the earth by volcanic eruptions. Thus, (2) is the correct answer. This one exception contradicts all the other choices.

18. **(4)** Both the diagram and the graphs show that transpiration (1), infiltration (2), and evaporation (3), account for the water that does not become precipitation. Thus, (4) is the correct answer.

19. **(4)** The diagram shows that precipitation falling as snow on mountain tops evaporates from the fallen snow and from glaciers formed from some of the snow. Thus, (2) is true. Also, the diagram shows glaciers moving down a mountain to the sea. If the glacier is in the colder parts of the arctic and antarctic regions, it will, upon reaching the ocean, break off and form icebergs, which eventually melt. If the glacier is in a more moderate climate, it will melt when it reaches lower altitudes on the mountainside. Thus, (3) is true. With (2) and (3) true, (4) is the correct answer.

20. **(3)** The hydrologic cycle *could* operate if only snow fell (1) or if rain were the only precipitation (2). And the cycle could operate if there was no groundwater infiltration (4). But if there was no wind to move evaporated moisture over the land from the sea the cycle would consist only of precipitation falling on the ocean, evaporating into the atmosphere, and again falling on the ocean—a process quite different from what we know as the hydrologic cycle. Thus, (3) is the correct answer.

21. **(2)** Paragraph five explains that the great pressure deep within the earth keeps the core from melting even though the temperature is above the

melting points of the metals that make up the core. Thus, (2) is the correct answer. Air is not necessary for melting the materials of the earth. This is shown by the fact that molten rock (lava) comes up to the surface from deep in the earth. Thus, (1) is not correct. The last sentence of the fifth paragraph says definitely that it is the great pressure that is responsible for the core being solid. Therefore, (3) cannot be correct.

22. (1) When the earth was molten, atoms of the elements were free to rise or sink in accordance with their weight. In general, heavier atoms, such as cobalt, nickel, and iron, sank toward the center of the earth. Thus, (1) is the correct answer. [*Note:* Since weight was not the only factor in the distribution of elements in the molten earth, we find some of each of the elements in the earth's crust.] A random mixing of elements alone could be expected to distribute elements fairly evenly throughout the earth, but this is not the case. Thus, (2) is not correct. Choice (3) states that the *lighter* elements were distributed in the core. This is contrary to what paragraphs four and five say. Thus, (3) is not correct.

23. (2) From the information in paragraphs four and five, we can calculate that the center of the earth is about 8000 miles from its surface. Using this figure to calculate the temperature at the center of the core, we multiply 80° by 2000, giving us 16,000° F. However, paragraph five says that the temperature of the core is only 5500° F. Therefore, the increase of 80° per mile is too great. This means that the rate of increase must become less as the depth becomes greater. Thus, (2) is correct. Since 90° is more than 80°, and the figure should be lower rather than higher, (4) is incorrect.

24. (3) The materials of mantle rock are loose materials, and erosion by water and wind, and the force of gravitation can easily move them to lowlands, exposing the bedrock of high places. Soil, sand, and other forms of mantle rock, being loose, offer little resistance to the forces of mountain building; therefore, the upthrusting mountains push through the mantle rock as they rise, exposing bedrock. Hence, they would be exposed. Thus (1) and (2) are both correct answers. So, choice (3) is the correct response.

25. (4) Paragraph one states that information about the earth's interior is obtained from studying lava and the recordings of shock waves from earthquakes and nuclear bomb testing. Since these are indirect methods, and since we cannot see, touch, or otherwise deal directly with the materials deep in the earth's interior, our information of the interior must be indirect. Thus, (4) is the correct answer. Although mathematical calculations are used in working out the information we have of the earth's interior, mathematical calculations are not a way of obtaining information on natural phenomena. Thus, (3) is not correct. Chemical analyses can be performed only on earth materials we can obtain, and we cannot obtain any directly from the deep interior of the earth. In addition, chemical analyses provide only one kind of information. Thus, (2) is not a correct choice.

THE SIMULATED TEST

DIRECTIONS: Read each of the following passages. Choose the BEST answer to each question. Then blacken the space under that number in the answer column. You may go back to the passage as often as necessary to answer the questions.

ANSWERS AND EXPLANATIONS APPEAR AT THE END OF THE TEST

S-I

The most conspicuous object inside the cell membrane is a roundish, and usually central, body made up of nucleoplasm—the nucleus. Its outer surface is a thin membrane made up of protein and lipid, a fatty substance. The electron microscope shows that this nuclear membrane is double-layered and honeycombed with very small openings through which tiny particles can pass out of or into the nucleus. If we use a vital stain (stain which does not kill protoplasm), such as methylene blue, we can see that the material inside the nuclear membrane is dense and contains definite threadlike particles. These make up the chromatin network, or chromosomes. The latter name means "color bodies," so-called because they stain readily. Chromosomes show more plainly when a cell is reproducing or dividing. Chromosomes are made up of deoxyribonucleic acid, usually called DNA, ribonucleic acid, usually called RNA, and nucleoproteins. DNA molecules are six-turned spirals wound around cylinders of nucleoproteins. Strung along the spiral are sections called genes. These act as patterns, recipes, or templates that cause cells to develop certain characteristics. These patterns are "translated into action" by RNA molecules, as RNA filters through the nuclear membrane into protoplasm around the nucleus. RNA molecules are found both inside and outside the nucleus, and especially where protein of growing protoplasm is being formed. RNA is a necessary component of the nucleus of all cells, making possible many cell activities.

Also within the nuclear membrane is usually one nucleolus, a structure which contains RNA. When a cell divides, the nucleolus breaks apart and "carries messages" in the so-called genetic code to protoplasm outside the nucleus. At the time of division, the nuclear membrane disappears. . . .

So the nucleus is a control center for cell activities. For example, without a nucleus, a cell cannot reproduce itself. Our red blood cells have no nuclei when they are mature, or fully developed, and so cannot divide and form more red blood cells. Biologists have transplanted the nucleus from a cell with certain characteristics into a related but differ-ent cell from which the nucleus had been removed. The cell receiving the nucleus then developed characteristics of the cell from which the nucleus had been taken.

The outer surface of the ectoplasm [the protoplasm near the cell's surface] is organized as a plasma membrane, also called a cell mem-brane. Everything entering or leaving a cell must pass through the plasma membrane. It is the place where a cell contacts its outside environment.

The plasma membrane is elastic and double layered. It has infold-ings and outpouchings which provide much surface area upon which molecules can gather and go through complex physical and chemical changes. It can make cell products, and can produce electrical cur-rents. . . .

1. A scientist transplants the nucleus of a muscle cell into a nerve cell from which the nucleus has been removed. The resulting mature cell will have the characteristics of
   (1) both nerve and muscle cells.
   (2) muscle cells.
   (3) nerve cells.
   (4) neither nerve nor muscle cells.

2. The purpose of using any kind of cell stain when viewing the cell under a microscope is to
   (1) keep the cell alive.
   (2) dry the cell material.
   (3) make structures within the cell visible.
   (4) keep the protoplasm moist.

3. When red blood cells reproduce
   (1) the nucleus divides first.
   (2) the nucleolus does not divide.
   (3) RNA translates into action the patterns found in DNA.
   (4) none of the above

4. When a cell divides, the protoplasm outside the nucleus is organized accord-ing to the genetic code by
   (1) the cylinders of DNA.
   (2) genetic messages carried by RNA of the nucleolus.
   (3) a double-layered nuclear membrane.
   (4) the electrical currents produced by the plasma membrane.

5. The nuclear membrane and the plasma membrane have in common that both are
   (1) elastic.   (3) double layered.
   (2) full of chromosomes.   (4) genes.

6. 1 2 3 4

6. In order to see to best advantage how the nuclear membrane carries out its functions during cell division,
   (1) a cell should be stained with methylene blue.
   (2) an electron microscope is necessary.
   (3) a vital stain must be used.
   (4) none of the above

7. 1 2 3 4

7. If it were possible for a cell to have RNA but no DNA the cell could not reproduce itself because
   (1) without genes, the RNA would not have a pattern for organizing the protoplasm of the new cell.
   (2) the RNA could not filter through the plasma membrane.
   (3) without electrical currents, the RNA would not have a supply of energy.
   (4) the new cell would lack a nucleus.

S-II

A gas consists of submicroscopic particles, called molecules, moving about in random fashion. The space occupied by the molecules is only a small fraction of the total volume of the gas. The rest of the volume is empty space.

The molecules of a gas are in constant, very rapid motion. As a result, the shape and volume of an unconfined gas is indefinite. A confined gas has the same shape and volume as that of its container.

The impact of the rapidly moving gas molecules against the walls of a container cause the gas to exert pressure on the container. Molecules rebounding from the walls and colliding with other molecules cause the pressure to spread equally throughout the gas. If the volume of the container is decreased, the number of impacts per unit area of the walls is increased, and consequently the total gas pressure is increased. If the volume of the container is increased, the number of impacts per unit area is decreased, and the gas pressure decreases.

From the behavior of the volume of a gas under pressure, the seventeenth century English scientist Robert Boyle deduced a law that bears his name. The law states, in effect: *If the temperature of a gas remains constant, the volume of the gas is inversely proportional to the pressure.* Or,

$$\frac{\text{new volume}}{\text{original volume}} = \frac{\text{original pressure}}{\text{new pressure}}.$$

Another way of expressing the same facts is:

$$\text{new volume} = \text{original volume} \times \frac{\text{original pressure}}{\text{new pressure}}.$$

In order that Boyle's Law hold, the container must be rigid; it must not change its size when the pressure changes.

8. The pressure of a gas on an inelastic container is caused by the
   (1) size of the molecules that make up the gas.
   (2) thickness of the walls of the container.
   (3) impact of the gas molecules on the walls of the container.
   (4) shape of the container.

   8. 1 2 3 4

9. If the temperature of a gas remains constant and the volume of the gas is 500 cc (cubic centimeters) at a pressure of 740 mm of mercury, at 370 mm (millimeters) pressure, the volume would be
   (1) 1000 cc.   (2) 600 cc.   (3) 250 cc.   (4) 185 cc.

   9. 1 2 3 4

10. The volume of gas in a toy balloon is 1000 cc at 250 mm of mercury. Another 1000 cc of gas are pumped into the balloon. According to Boyle's Law, the pressure becomes
    (1) 500 mm.   (3) 1550 mm.
    (2) 2000 mm.   (4) none of the above

    10. 1 2 3 4

11. 1   2   3   4
    ‖ ‖ ‖ ‖

11. If a gas is contained in a cube and the pressure on one wall of the cube is 10 pounds per square inch, the pressure on each of the other walls is
(1)   50 pounds per square inch.
(2)   60 pounds per square inch.
(3)   10 pounds per square inch.
(4)   2 pounds per square inch.

12. 1   2   3   4
    ‖ ‖ ‖ ‖

12. Suppose that a gas is contained in a cube and the pressure within the cube is 24 pounds per square inch. The volume of the cube is halved and no gas is removed. The pressure on one wall of the cube will then be
(1)   4 pounds per square inch.
(2)   48 pounds per square inch.
(3)   8 pounds per square inch.
(4)   none of the above

13. 1   2   3   4
    ‖ ‖ ‖ ‖

13. The volume of a gas-filled container is doubled. This means that the number of impacts of gas molecules on the walls of the container is
(1)   halved.   (3)   tripled.
(2)   doubled.   (4)   quadrupled.

S-III

The teeth are very important in preparing food for digestion. There are three types of teeth, and each type has special work to do. The teeth in the front of the mouth are called incisors. They are used to cut large pieces of food into smaller ones. You use incisors, for example, when you eat an apple.

Next are fang-shaped teeth called canines, or canine teeth. In dogs and other meat-eating animals these teeth are very important in tearing meat off a bone and in fighting and catching prey; hence the name canine, or dog-like. In man, the roots of the upper canine teeth are buried so deep in the skull that they nearly reach the eye socket. For this reason the upper canines in man are sometimes called eye teeth.

In an adult with a full set of teeth, there are ten grinding teeth in each jaw, located behind the canines. These are called the premolars and the molars. They are used to crush and grind food.

Only the beginnings of our permanent teeth are in the jaws at birth. Before the permanent teeth appear, however, twenty baby, or milk, teeth come in. These temporary teeth begin to loosen at about the sixth year. Their roots are gradually absorbed, and they are pushed away from the jaw bone by the growth of the permanent teeth. Between the sixth and the thirteenth year almost all of the permanent teeth appear in the mouth. The wisdom teeth, or third molars, usually do not appear until years later. When all his teeth are in, man has thirty-two of them.

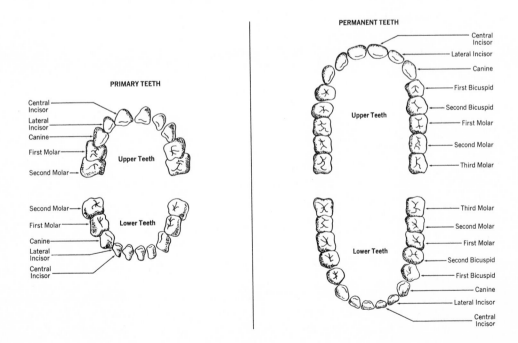

The outer layer of each tooth is composed of enamel. Enamel is the hardest substance in your body. Under the enamel is a layer of softer, bonelike material called dentine. This surrounds the central pulp cavity that contains the nerves and blood vessels present in every tooth.

Teeth, including even their hard enamel coverings, are subject to decay. What leads to tooth decay, or caries, is not completely known. . . . Foods high in sugar content—candy and cake, for example—seem to promote tooth decay. Such foods encourage the growth of bacteria that produce acid. It is thought that this acid causes the enamel to decay.

Minute amounts of chemicals called fluorides in drinking water promote healthy teeth by preventing tooth decay. In some areas of our country, water as it comes from wells contains fluorides. In areas where this is not the case, many communities are adding fluorides to their water supplies. This action has been shown to reduce tooth decay by as much as two-thirds. No known ill effects result from the addition of the proper amount of fluorides to the water.

The study of the effects of fluoridation on a community's health usually means that at least two cities must be studied. Fluorides are added to the water supply of one city, but no fluorides to that of the second city, [which is known as the control city]. The two cities should be very much alike in all of the factors that may affect the health of their citizens. . . .

14. Cows are not handicapped by lack of canine teeth because cows
    (1)   do not catch prey.
    (2)   eat nuts and seeds.
    (3)   do not tear meat off bones.
    (4)   both (1) and (3) of the above

15. Tales of travelers in ancient times tell of finding here and there a people with strikingly healthy teeth. These peoples' dental health might have been due to
    (1)   brushing their teeth after every meal.
    (2)   their being vegetarians.
    (3)   naturally fluoridated drinking water.
    (4)   a secret formula for tooth paste.

16. If a five-year-old boy with some decayed teeth is taught and practices good dental hygiene, he will
    (1)   be able to save his undecayed teeth for use in his adult life.
    (2)   probably have a full set of good teeth in his adult years.
    (3)   lose all his teeth no matter what he does.
    (4)   both (2) and (3) of the above

17. It would not be sensible to tell a small child being taught the proper way to brush his teeth that he should give particular attention to his third molars, or wisdom teeth, because
    (1)   a child's wisdom teeth are the first permanent teeth to grow in.
    (2)   wisdom teeth are not needed for chewing children's foods.
    (3)   the shape of a child's wisdom teeth makes them much less susceptible to decay.
    (4)   none of the above

18. When the results of fluoridation of a community's water supply are studied
    (1)   they must be compared with a similar community that has not received
           fluoridated water.
    (2)   it must be done within a period of two years.
    (3)   a control is necessary.
    (4)   both (1) and (3) of the above

18. 1 2 3 4

19. Man has three kinds of teeth: cutting, grinding, and tearing, because
    (1)   man eats both plant foods and meat.
    (2)   man evolved from three different kinds of animals.
    (3)   random evolution gave man his different kinds of teeth.
    (4)   all of the above

19. 1 2 3 4

20. Tooth decay is caused by
    (1)   bacteria.
    (2)   foods having a high sugar content.
    (3)   acid.
    (4)   all of the above

20. 1 2 3 4

S-IV

Water has been chosen as a standard for comparison for several physical units. Water is used in this way because it is abundant, it is widely distributed, it is stable, and it is easily purified.

A gram is defined in terms of water; it is the weight of one milliliter of pure water at 4° C. The temperature 4° C was indicated because a milliliter of water weighs less when it is either warmer than 4° C or colder than 4° C. We say that the greatest density of water is at 4° C.

Density is weight per unit volume. It is pounds per cubic foot, or kilograms per liter, or grams per milliliter, etc. Since the weight of one milliliter of water is one gram, its density is one gram per milliliter.

The lightness or heaviness of a substance is often described by comparing its density with the density of water [at 4° C]. Such a comparison is known as specific weight or specific gravity. By saying that the specific gravity of gold is 19.3, we simply mean that gold is 19.3 times as heavy as an equal volume of water.

The fixed points on the centigrade [or Celsius] thermometer scale were chosen with reference to water. Zero degrees centigrade is the freezing point of water and 100° C is the boiling point of water under normal atmospheric pressure (760 mm of mercury).

A thermometer shows temperature, or the intensity of heat, which depends on the average kinetic energy of the molecules of a substance. Temperature alone, however, is not an indication of the total amount of heat which a substance possesses. The total amount of heat depends upon the total molecular energy. A teacup of boiling water, for example, will not melt as much snow as a gallon of water at room temperature. There is considerably more heat energy in the gallon than there is in the cupful. You need more than a thermometer, in other words, to measure the total amount of heat in a cup of water or liberated by a burning fuel or by any other source of heat.

The total amount of heat involved in any chemical or physical process may be expressed in calories, which are defined in terms of water. A calorie (abbreviated cal.) is the amount of heat required to raise the temperature of one gram of water one degree centigrade.

The calorie is a small metric heat unit. A large unit, called a kilogram-calorie (or kilocalorie [kcal], or large calorie, or Calorie) is used to express heat values, such as those of foods. A kilocalorie is the amount of heat required to raise the temperature of 1 kilogram of water 1° C, and is equal to 1000 small calories.

21. 1 2 3 4

21. If ten milliliters of mercury weigh 135.5 grams, how much denser is mercury than water?

(1) 13.6 times

(2) 27.1 times

(3) 1.35 times

(4) 2.71 times

22. A scientist burns a whole cigarette to ashes. He can measure the total amount of heat given off by the burning cigarette

    (1)   directly by means of a thermometer.

    (2)   by measuring the average kinetic energy of the molecules of the substances that make up the cigarette.

    (3)   by determining the total molecular energy of the substances that make up the cigarette.

    (4)   both (1) and (3) of the above

22. 1 2 3 4

23. Suppose a glass contains 100 ml of water at 50° C. The glass is put into a refrigerator and the temperature of the water drops to 5° C. The number of calories of heat gained by air in the refrigerator is

    (1) 4500.   (2) 500.   (3) 450.   (4) 5000.

23. 1 2 3 4

24. A sugar substitute is advertised as having only 5 Calories per teaspoonful, as compared to 50 Calories for a teaspoonful of cane sugar. This means that the sugar substitute, when compared to cane sugar,

    (1)   provides the body with more energy.

    (2)   is more healthful.

    (3)   provides the body with less energy.

    (4)   all of the above

24. 1 2 3 4

25. The specific gravity of water at 1° C, when compared to water at 4° C, is

    (1)   greater.

    (2)   less.

    (3)   the same.

    (4)   not possible to determine.

25. 1 2 3 4

26. In the regions of the world where bodies of water freeze at some time during the year, fish owe their lives to the fact that

    (1)   the density of water is greatest at 4° C.

    (2)   ice weighs less than water at 4° C.

    (3)   less dense substances float on denser substances.

    (4)   all of the above

26. 1 2 3 4

27. The number of calories in a cup of water at 100° C, when compared to the number of calories in a gallon jug of water at 20° C (room temperature), is

    (1)   less.   (3)   the same.

    (2)   more.   (4)   indeterminable.

27. 1 2 3 4

S-V

The communities of organisms that invade . . . "new" living spaces are not stable; they are followed by a succession of communities before a dynamic equilibrium is established.

We shall consider only one example and, to simplify the description, limit our attention to plants (though each community, of course, is made up of other organisms). The surface of bare rock is very warm by day and cold at night. Water cannot soak in, so that shortly after a rain the rock is dry. Under such conditions few organisms can exist. Of these few, lichens are the only ones visible to the naked eye. Land snails may sometimes consume these producers; microscopic decomposers may decay the lichens when they die.

The lichens produce acids that gradually make crevices in the rock surface. Small quantities of the decaying lichens and bits of dust, blown by the wind, collect in these crevices. Thus a simple soil is formed. After rains, this soil will hold small quantities of water for a time. Mosses, which could not survive on the solid rock surface, can live in these small quantities of soil. The "bodies" of mosses are likely to be larger than those of lichens; they trap more windblown dust, and they form more soil when they die. The increase in soil favors the growth of the mosses. Moreover, since mosses carry on photosynthesis more effectively than lichens, the mosses eventually overgrow the lichens. Thus a "moss community" succeeds a "lichen community."

But the moss community, too, will pass away. In the steadily accumulating soil, the seeds of larger plants are able to germinate. These larger plants do not necessarily displace the mosses, but as they grow upward, they hide the mosses from view. Being larger, they contribute more to the developing soil, and having roots, they push down into cracks in the rock, forming ever deeper pockets of soil on the rock surface. . . . Succession continues until a forest community develops, though the process may require hundreds of years. The forest community, once it is formed, may then persist for tens of thousands of years, in dynamic equilibrium.

28. During a large part of the early history of the earth, the land was bare rock. When plants finally began to grow on land, the first plants probably were somewhat like modern
    (1) lichens.   (3) mosses.
    (2) trees.   (4) ferns.

29. As succession in a plant community continues, the rate of formation of soil
    (1) decreases.   (3) increases.
    (2) remains the same. (4) stops.

30. Two rocks are near each other, one rock flat and horizontal, the other flat and steeply inclined. A moss community is more likely to develop first
    (1) by chance on either rock.   (3) on the inclined rock.
    (2) on the flat rock.   (4) on the rounded, slanted rock.

31. Over thousands of years, a forest community grew in soil where once there was only bare rock. Fire destroys the forest. For a new forest community to grow in the same place will take

31. 1 2 3 4

  (1) less time.
  (2) longer.
  (3) about the same time.
  (4) an unpredictable length of time.

32. In certain parts of the world, lichens and mosses grow on rocks, but are never succeeded by any other plants. A possible reason for this lack of succession might be

32. 1 2 3 4

  (1) the conditions for the growth of other plants are lacking.
  (2) these particular lichens and mosses grow faster and better than other plants and win the battle for survival.
  (3) the lichens and mosses are eaten by animals before they can decay and make soil.
  (4) lichens and mosses can grow in only certain kinds of soil, which is not fertile for any other kinds of plants.

33. In addition to sun and water, which are necessary for the process of photosynthesis, another important climatic agent in the succession of plants is

33. 1 2 3 4

  (1) darkness.
  (2) wind.
  (3) snow.
  (4) alternating warm and cold seasons.

S-VI

If we examine a geographical globe of the earth, we find that it is covered by a network of lines intersecting each other at right angles. Those that run from the North Pole to the South Pole are called *meridians of longitude*. They are reference lines by which we can measure distances east and west. The unit of measurement is the degree. The meridian at 0° is called the *prime meridian* and runs through the former site of the British Royal Observatory at Greenwich, England. The degrees then run east and west to 180°, which is in the Pacific Ocean.

Distance from the equator to the poles is measured in degrees of *latitude*. Unlike the meridians of longitude which meet at the poles, the lines by which latitude is measured are concentric parallel circles. These circles are called *parallels* of latitude. Zero degrees of latitude is at the equator and 90° is at either pole. North latitude includes all the parallels that can be drawn between the equator and the North Pole. Similarly, south latitude includes all those parallels between the equator and the South Pole.

A degree of latitude is divided into 60 minutes of latitude, and the approximate length of 1 minute is 1.852 kilometers, or $1\frac{1}{6}$ miles. Seamen have adopted this distance as a measure of distance and have called it the nautical mile. The minute of arc is divided into 60 seconds, 1 second being approximately 31 meters, or 102 feet, in length.

The network of intersecting lines is based on the geometric principle that two lines intersect at only one point. So, by stating the intersection of a meridian of longitude and a parallel of latitude, we locate one and only one point on earth. Thus, giving latitude and longitude locates any place on earth. For example, 30° north latitude and 90° west longitude locate New Orleans, Louisiana.

34. 1 2 3 4

34. Latitude is measured from
   (1) the equator.
   (2) Greenwich, England.
   (3) the prime meridian.
   (4) none of the above

35. 1 2 3 4

35. The maximum number of degrees of longitude through which a ship could sail in one direction is
   (1) 360. (2) 90. (3) 180. (4) 30.

36. 1 2 3 4

36. One degree of latitude equals about
   (1) 16 miles.
   (2) 140 miles.
   (3) 7 miles.
   (4) 70 miles.

37. 1 2 3 4

37. New Orleans is 30° north of the equator. The distance in miles from New Orleans to the North Pole is
   (1) 6300.
   (2) 4200.
   (3) 2100.
   (4) 8400.

38. Assuming that the earth is a perfect sphere, one degree of latitude is equal to one degree of longitude

 (1) at the equator.
 (2) nowhere on earth.
 (3) at the poles.
 (4) midway between the prime meridian and the equator.

38. 1 2 3 4

39. The longitude of East St. Louis, Illinois, is 90°

 (1) south. (3) east.
 (2) west. (4) north.

39. 1 2 3 4

40. When traveling from the South Pole, you must go to

 (1) lower latitudes. (3) higher latitudes.
 (2) west longitudes. (4) east longitudes.

40. 1 2 3 4

S-VII

[Certain] diseases have indirect methods of transmission, frequently involving an *alternation of hosts*. Malaria, a disease that has almost disappeared from the United States but that is still among the most common plagues of man in the tropics, passes from man to the *Anopheles* mosquito to man. . . . [The mosquito is called a *vector* of the disease.]

The malarial parasite . . . has a complex life history. It enters the bloodstream of man through the bite of a mosquito and travels to the liver. Here it multiplies. The offspring move back into the bloodstream, where they enter red blood cells and continue to multiply—destroying the red cells as they do so. The parasite usually multiplies by simply dividing, but from time to time special forms are produced that can be called "male" and "female." If the normal forms are picked up by a mosquito while it is sucking blood, they die in the mosquito's stomach. But if the male and female forms are picked up, a male parasite may produce a flagellated structure that unites with a female parasite, forming a single new individual. This new form then squeezes through the stomach wall of the mosquito and starts to divide, eventually forming a cluster of hundreds of individuals within the insect. These individuals presently burst free and migrate through the mosquito body to the salivary glands, where they remain until the mosquito next takes a blood meal.

When a mosquito "bites," it probes through the skin until it locates a small blood vessel or, by breaking several vessels, forms a small pool of blood. Blood, of course, clots, and thus it might plug up the mosquito's mouthparts; but this usually does not happen. The mosquito injects some of its saliva into the blood, and in most species this saliva contains a substance that prevents clotting. If the mosquito has malarial parasites in its salivary glands, these are injected along with the saliva, and the parasite has found a new, human host.

41. 1 2 3 4

41. Malaria is transmitted from one person to another by
    (1)   an insect.
    (2)   coughing and sneezing.
    (3)   eating infected food.
    (4)   all of the above

42. 1 2 3 4

42. A man is bitten by an *Anopheles* mosquito which on the previous day bit another man who was suffering from malaria. The chances of the man bitten last becoming infected with malaria are
    (1)   good.
    (2)   uncertain.
    (3)   poor.
    (4)   absolutely certain.

43. 1 2 3 4

43. When a mosquito bites, it injects saliva into its victim. This is of advantage to the mosquito because it
    (1)   poisons the victim.
    (2)   transmits malaria.
    (3)   prevents the victim's blood from clotting in the mosquito's mouthparts.
    (4)   causes the bite to itch.

44. If mosquitoes worried about malaria, they would call man a
    (1) vector.
    (3) plasmodium.
    (2) parasite.
    (4) all of the above

44. 1 2 3 4

45. Suppose that a certain tropical country has a large proportion of its population ill with malaria. Suppose, also, that these people can use only one at a time the following ways of combating the disease. Their first choice should be to
    (1) give everyone medicine that will cure malaria.
    (2) get rid of mosquitoes.
    (3) build hospitals.
    (4) give injections only to people ill with malaria.

45. 1 2 3 4

46. A mosquito which had never bitten a man before sucks blood from a man ill with malaria. Ten seconds later, the mosquito bites a man who never had malaria. The second man will
    (1) not become ill with malaria.
    (2) may or may not become ill with malaria.
    (3) become ill with malaria.
    (4) none of the above

46. 1 2 3 4

S-VIII

Chemistry had a humble origin. Like every other science, it began with simple discoveries which were useful to man. The primitive chemistry of the Egyptians was concerned with crude medicine and technology. By trial and error they discovered the curative or harmful properties of the juices of plants.... The Egyptians were not interested in chemical theories but only in the technical applications which brought them wealth and power.

The Greek philosophers studied chemistry for a different reason. The Greeks were not interested in the material gain to be derived from chemistry; to them knowledge was its own reward....

The Greeks believed that all substances were derived from four basic "elements"—earth, water, air, and fire. These four "elements," they believed, were combined in different proportions to make all substances in the universe.... It was thought that a substance was broken down into its elements when it burned. For example, wood is a complex substance. When it burns, fire is observed, smoke or "air" rises, water can be seen boiling from the wood, and the ash which remains is "earth." Thus, fire, air, water, and earth were believed to be the fundamental "building blocks" of which wood is composed.

Once this theory was accepted, it followed quite naturally that one substance could be changed into another merely by varying the proportions of the original constituents. Thus was born the idea of the transmutation of elements, a concept that dominated chemistry for many centuries.

In the Middle Ages chemists, or rather alchemists as they were then called, developed certain beliefs which formed the theoretical bases of their science and guided them in their experimental work. They believed that man and everything in nature, even a metal, is ever striving toward perfection. They argued that the perfect metal is gold since, (1) it does not tarnish in the air; (2) it resists the action of acids; and (3) it is not affected, as other metals are, when it is heated with sulfur. To them it seemed that all metals were striving toward gold, and the only difference between gold and another metal such as lead was one of age or maturity.

The work of the alchemists was founded upon this fundamental misconception of the unity of nature. They believed it was possible to hurry the slow process of nature and even to hasten the conversion of the "baser" metals into gold. Thus the transmutation of one metal into another became the chief aim of the alchemist.

The work of the alchemist continued for many centuries. It failed because it was based upon a false premise. The alchemist assumed, at the outset, that he understood the ways of nature and he never questioned the validity of his assumption that nature is striving toward perfection. ... Nevertheless, the work of the alchemist was not in vain. The wide range of the search led to much factual knowledge; new forms of apparatus were devised; and above all, the chemist learned to beware of false hypotheses. Paradoxically, alchemy, founded upon fiction, thus paved the way for the development of chemistry, founded upon fact.

47. The ancient alchemist should not be classified as a true scientist mainly because
    (1)   he believed in "base" elements.
    (2)   he did not attempt to verify his hypotheses.
    (3)   he believed that gold was a perfect metal.
    (4)   the transmutation of one metal into another was his chief aim.

48. The most effective methods the ancient Egyptians developed for producing chemical products
    (1)   were based on theory.
    (2)   depended upon their comprehension of the unity of nature.
    (3)   had as their foundation a trial-and-error approach.
    (4)   both (1) and (2) of the above

49. An interest in chemistry only as an abstract theory
    (1)   gave rise to the positive fruits of alchemy.
    (2)   guided the Greeks in their experimental work.
    (3)   was typical of the Greek philosophers' concern with chemistry.
    (4)   led to the discovery of gold.

50. The Greeks thought that by exposing a substance to fire
    (1)   it would absorb other elements.
    (2)   it would oxidize.
    (3)   the fire would absorb some elementary properties of the substance.
    (4)   it would burn and break down into its constituent elements.

51. With the end of the Middle Ages, alchemy
    (1)   disappeared without a trace.
    (2)   continued to flourish.
    (3)   provided a body of knowledge that paved the way to the science of chemistry.
    (4)   none of the above

52. Although the alchemists' work was based on false premises, it
    (1)   was a complete waste of time.
    (2)   led to the accumulation of much factual knowledge and the devising of new chemical apparatus.
    (3)   taught the chemist to beware of false hypotheses.
    (4)   both (2) and (3) of the above.

53. In the history of chemistry, the Egyptians
    (1)   followed the lead of the Greeks.
    (2)   were particularly interested in chemical theories.
    (3)   divided all substances into "elements."
    (4)   none of the above

S-IX

The Nitrogen Cycle

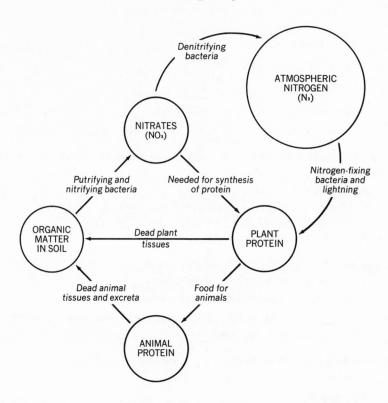

Nitrogen is the most abundant element in the atmosphere, making up 78 percent of the volume of dry air. Combined with other elements, nitrogen occurs in a great number of compounds, both inorganic and organic. The chief inorganic compound is the salt, sodium nitrate. Nitrogen is the most important element in proteins, and proteins are the basic constituents of protoplasm. Hence, nitrogen is as vital to life as oxygen is.

A complex relationship exists between plants and animals and nitrogen. This relationship is known as the *nitrogen cycle*.

Briefly, the cycle operates in the following manner. Certain bacteria, known as nitrogen-fixing bacteria, take gaseous nitrogen directly from the atmosphere and convert the nitrogen into part of their own protoplasm. Colonies of these bacteria live on the roots of certain plants called legumes. Examples of legumes are alfalfa, soy beans, and clover. Legumes, in their growth, make use of some of the nitrogen-containing substances in the protoplasm of the bacteria on their roots. These substances are used in the formation of plant proteins.

Plants die and are decomposed by certain kinds of bacteria and molds, and the former plant proteins become nitrogen-containing compounds in the soil. These compounds, mostly nitrates, can be used by any plants to build proteins.

Herbivorous animals eat plants and some of the plants' proteins (with their nitrogen) become animal protein. The animals excrete nitrogen-containing compounds in their waste matter which eventually becomes part of the soil. Animals die and decomposers (certain bacteria and fungi) break down animal proteins, making them part of the soil along with decomposed plant proteins. In this manner, animal protein becomes a source of nitrogen for plants.

Some of the nitrates in the soil are acted upon directly by so-called denitrifying bacteria, which change the nitrates to nitrous oxide, which escapes into the atmosphere where it eventually splits into nitrogen and oxygen. Thus, gaseous nitrogen is returned to the atmosphere, and the nitrogen cycle is complete.

A relatively small amount of nitrogen in the air is converted by lightning into oxides of nitrogen. These combine with water vapor, forming dilute nitric acid which is carried by rain into the soil. Here nitrates are formed and are used by plants.

54. A cycle is a series of events that repeat themselves one or more times. The diagram shows that the nitrogen cycle involves more than one cycle. There are a total of
   (1)   two cycles.   (3)   four cycles.
   (2)   three cycles.   (4)   five cycles.

    54. 1 2 3 4

55. Before the twentieth century, farmers would plant a field with food crops for one or two years, then, in a third year, plant the field with clover or alfalfa and plough this crop into the soil. They did this in order to
   (1)   increase the amount of nitrogen in the soil.
   (2)   give the soil a rest from bearing food crops.
   (3)   have the denitrifying bacteria put nitrogen into the soil.
   (4)   none of the above

    55. 1 2 3 4

56. If nitrogen-fixing bacteria suddenly were to disappear from earth, the nitrogen cycle could continue because of the action of
   (1)   plants.   (3)   legumes.
   (2)   lightning.   (4)   denitrifying bacteria.

    56. 1 2 3 4

57. From the nitrogen cycle, it is possible to make a good guess that the first living things on land were
   (1)   animals.   (3)   amphibians.
   (2)   plants.   (4)   crawling fish.

    57. 1 2 3 4

58. Since there were no legumes before the first plants lived on land (plants lived in the seas and other bodies of water before invading the land), the nitrogen compounds needed by land plants probably were put into the earth's early soil by
   (1)   lightning.   (3)   water plants.
   (2)   sunlight.   (4)   both (1) and (3) of the above

    58. 1 2 3 4

59. 1   2   3   4
     || || || ||

59. Nitrogen is important to animal life because it is a
    (1) necessary part of the air that all animals use in the process of respiration.
    (2) major constituent of protoplasm.
    (3) nourishing food.
    (4) all of the above

S-X

Anyone in possession of a small telescope can avail himself of the opportunity to observe the greatest wonder of the solar system—Saturn's rings. In the equatorial plane of the planet, a system of perfectly circular rings stretches out from 9000 to 47,000 miles from the surface of Saturn, whose diameter is 75,000 miles, or almost ten times that of the earth. There are three principle rings; the outer two brilliantly shining in reflected sunlight and separated by a narrow space, and the third, an inner "gray" ring conspicuous only where it passes over the sunlit disk of Saturn as a dark band. . . .

The satellites of the planets may have been formed . . . from nebulous or dust rings attached to each planet. All but one of the original rings of the solar system have disappeared; only Saturn's rings remain as living testimony of the old days of creation.

What prevented the rings of Saturn from condensing into one or several satellites, to join the known ten and the probable host of small unknown satellites of the planet? The answer is Saturn itself, by virtue of tidal force. The tidal force is like that exercised by the moon on the earth, and, reciprocally, by the earth on the moon. . . . Saturn is 95 times heavier than the earth, or 7600 times more massive than the moon, and the rings are much nearer to Saturn's surface than the moon is to the earth. A satellite placed at the distance of its rings from Saturn would be subject to enormous tidal force, sufficient to tear it to pieces even were it made of solid rock. The rings are too close to Saturn for the formation of a satellite.

. . . From the high reflecting power of the bright rings, similar to that of snow, and from certain spectroscopic evidence, it appears probable that the rings consist of ice crystals or snowflakes into which a water vapor envelope condensed at a time when the solar system came into being. Each of these snowflakes revolves around Saturn in its own orbit, like a tiny satellite; they are tightly packed, one beside another, occasionally "elbowing" one another, thus producing friction. This friction has caused the rings to become regular circular disks of an extremely small thickness; the average diameter is equal to the average diameter of one particle only, perhaps a few inches, or even less. In any case, although the actual thickness of the rings is unknown, it cannot be more than about 1000 feet; otherwise the rings would have influenced, by their gravitation, the motion of Saturn's satellites. No such influence has been observed.

60. The earth's natural satellite, the moon, was able to form from a ring of matter that once surrounded the earth because the
    (1)   moon is farther from the earth than Saturn's rings are from that planet.
    (2)   earth weighs less than Saturn.

60. 1   2   3   4

(3)   tidal force of the earth on its ring was less than Saturn's tidal force on its rings.

(4)   all of the above

61. 1 2 3 4

61.   Saturn's inner ring can be seen even with a small telescope

(1)   when Saturn is viewed from any position.

(2)   only when Saturn is viewed so that the inner ring passes over Saturn's sunlit disk.

(3)   only when Saturn's rings are seen edge-on.

(4)   none of the above

62. 1 2 3 4

62.   Saturn has no satellites that are as close to its surface as Saturn's rings because

(1)   a satellite would collide with the rings and break up.

(2)   no sooner did a satellite form than it fell to the planet's surface.

(3)   it once had nearby satellites but they were moving so fast that they pulled away from the planet.

(4)   Saturn's tidal force would break up a satellite as close to the planet's surface as the rings are.

63. 1 2 3 4

63.   Astronomers believe Saturn's rings to be

(1)   a recent development in the solar system.

(2)   dust rings formed from matter thrown off by volcanoes that once were active on the planet.

(3)   a model of one stage in the development of the solar system.

(4)   both (1) and (3) of the above

64. 1 2 3 4

64.   In addition to Saturn's rings, that planet has

(1)   no other satellites.

(2)   one moon 7600 times as massive as the earth's moon.

(3)   ten known satellites.

(4)   one satellite 95 times as heavy as earth.

65. 1 2 3 4

65.   Saturn's rings are

(1)   like the rings of its nearby neighbors, the planets Jupiter and Uranus.

(2)   probably composed of small pieces of rock.

(3)   as thick as half of Saturn's diameter.

(4)   none of the above

ANSWERS AND EXPLANATIONS
FOR THE SIMULATED TEST

1. **(2)** Paragraph three states that when the nucleus of a cell of one type is transplanted into a cell of another type from which the nucleus has been removed, the second cell develops the characteristics of the cell from which the nucleus was taken. Therefore, the nerve cell would develop the characteristics of the muscle cell. Thus, (2) is the correct answer.

2. **(3)** Paragraph one states that if we use a certain kind of stain on a cell, we will then be able to see certain structures within the nucleus. From this we can reason that a stain is needed to enable us to see the structures. Thus, (3) is the correct answer. The same paragraph says that if a vital stain is used, the stain will not kill the protoplasm. However, the question asks simply why any kind of cell stain is used, not particularly a vital stain. Hence, (1) is not a correct choice. Nothing is said in the passage about drying cell material (2), nor about keeping protoplasm moist (4). Hence, (2) and (4) are not correct.

3. **(4)** Paragraph three says that without a nucleus a cell cannot reproduce and that red blood cells have no nucleus. Therefore, all the choices are incorrect, and (4) is the proper answer.

4. **(2)** Paragraph two states that when a cell divides, the nucleolus breaks apart and carries messages in the genetic code to protoplasm outside the nucleus. Thus, (2) is the correct answer. Paragraph one describes DNA as being spiral and nucleoproteins as being cylinders. Hence, (1) cannot be correct. Paragraph one describes several characteristics of the nuclear membrane, but does not give any function for it. So, (3) is not correct. Paragraph five notes that the plasma membrane can produce electrical currents, but does not connect them in any way to cell division. Hence, (4) is not correct.

5. **(3)** The third sentence of paragraph one describes the nuclear membrane as double layered, and the first sentence of the last paragraph says that the plasma membrane is both double layered and elastic, but the description in the first paragraph of the nuclear membrane does not describe that membrane as being elastic. Hence, (1) is not correct. The first paragraph says that chromosomes may be found in the nucleus itself, but does not say anything about chromosomes being in the membrane. Thus, (2) is incorrect. Genes are described, in paragraph one, as sections of the spiral DNA molecules; no connection between genes and the nuclear or plasma membranes is described. Hence, (4) is incorrect.

6. **(4)** Paragraph two says that during cell division, the nuclear membrane disappears. Therefore, the nuclear membrane does not carry out any functions during cell division. Thus, (4) is the correct answer.

7. **(1)** Paragraph one says that those parts of DNA molecules called genes act as patterns that cause cells to develop certain characteristics. These

patterns are translated into action by RNA molecules. Without the DNA molecules, the RNA molecules would not have patterns for organizing the protoplasm of the new cell. Thus, (1) is the correct answer. Paragraph one does not make any connection between DNA and the fact that RNA molecules filter through the nuclear membrane. Thus, (2) is not correct. Electrical currents are mentioned as being products of the plasma membrane, and no connection is made between them and RNA, DNA, or cell reproduction. Thus, (3) is not correct. If there were no DNA to provide genes as patterns for reproduction, no new cell could be formed. Hence, (4) is not correct.

8. **(3)** The first sentence of paragraph three directly states, in slightly different words, choice (3), which is the correct answer. The passage does not mention the size of molecules as a cause of gas pressure. Thus, (1) is not correct. As long as the walls of the container are inelastic, their thickness is not involved in the number of impacts upon them by the molecules of the gas. Therefore, the thickness of the walls of a container will not have anything to do with causing gas pressure. Thus, (2) is not correct. Paragraph two states that a confined gas completely fills its container; and paragraph three explains how pressure is spread equally throughout a gas. Hence, the shape of a container would not have anything to do with causing gas pressure. Thus, (4) is not a correct choice.

9. **(1)** To find the pressure of the gas at 370 mm, we use Boyle's equation. We have given the original volume, 500 cc; the original pressure, 740 mm; and the new pressure, 370 mm. Then,

$$\text{new volume} = \text{original volume} \times \frac{\text{original pressure}}{\text{new pressure}}$$
$$= 500 \times \frac{740}{370}$$
$$= 500 \times 2$$
$$= 1000 \text{ cc, the new volume.}$$

Thus, (1) is the correct answer. One way of roughly checking your answer is to keep in mind that the volume of a gas is *inversely* proportional to the pressure. In this problem, the pressure decreases, so the volume must increase. Choices (2), (3), and (4) all involve volumes less than the original volume, and thus must be wrong.

10. **(4)** The last paragraph of the passage says that for Boyle's Law to hold, the gas container must not change its size as the pressure changes. A balloon is elastic and does change its size as pressure within changes; therefore, Boyle's Law does not hold. Thus, (4) is the correct answer.

11. **(3)** Paragraph three says that pressure is spread equally throughout a gas. Therefore, the pressure on each wall of the cube will be the same as the pressure on any other wall. Since the pressure on one wall is 10 pounds per square inch, the pressure on each wall is 10 pounds per square inch. Thus, (3) is the correct answer.

12. (2) To find the pressure after the volume of the cube has changed, we use Boyle's Law. We are given an original pressure of 24 pounds per square inch, but we are not given original or new volume in cubic units. We can still solve the problem by taking the original volume to be one unit. Then the new volume will be one-half (0.5) unit. Let the new pressure be p. Using Boyle's equation, we have

$$\frac{\text{new volume}}{\text{original volume}} = \frac{\text{original pressure}}{\text{new pressure}}$$

Substituting the given values in the equation:

$$\frac{0.5}{1} = \frac{24}{p}$$

Multiplying both sides of the equation by p:

$$0.5p = 24$$

Solving:

$$p = \frac{24}{0.5}$$
$$p = 48$$

The new pressure is 48 pounds per square inch. Paragraph three says that the pressure of a contained gas is spread equally throughout the gas. Therefore, the pressure on any wall of the cube is 48 pounds per square inch. Thus, (2) is the correct answer.

13. (1) According to Boyle's Law, the pressure of a gas is inversely proportional to the volume. In this question, we are told that the volume doubles; therefore, the pressure will be halved. Since, according to paragraph three, the pressure of a gas on the walls of its container is due to the impacts of the molecules on the walls of the container, if the pressure is halved, the number of impacts will be halved. Thus, (1) is the correct answer.

14. (4) Canine teeth, paragraph two states, are used for tearing meat off bones and for catching prey. Cows, which do not eat meat nor hunt prey, have no use for canine teeth. Thus (1) and (3) are both true, making (4) the correct answer. Cows do not ordinarily eat nuts and seeds, so (2) is incorrect.

15. (3) Although ancient peoples used toothpicks, they did not have tooth-brushes and toothpaste; thus (1) and (4) are not correct. Sweet berries contain sugar, which, the passage states, causes tooth decay. Hence, (2) is not correct. The passage states that some water is naturally fluoridated and that drinking fluoridated water has been shown to lessen tooth decay. Thus, (3) is the correct answer.

16. (4) He will not be able to save any of his teeth, because a five-year-old has baby teeth, which normally fall out and are replaced by adult teeth; therefore, (1) is incorrect. If he practices good dental hygiene,

he will keep his future adult teeth in good condition, making (2) a correct choice. Good dental hygiene will save those of his baby teeth that are not decayed only until they fall out naturally; hence, (3) is a correct choice. With (2) and (3) both correct, (4) is the correct answer.

17. **(4)** A child has no wisdom teeth. Paragraph four states that wisdom teeth appear after the rest of the permanent teeth, all of which do not grow in until adolescence. Thus, (1), (2), and (3) are wrong, and (4) is the correct answer.

18. **(4)** The passage explains that in a community-wide fluoridation experiment, at least one community, having as its main difference the lack of fluoridated water, is needed as a control. Thus, (1) and (3) are true. Nothing is said in the passage about a two-year time limit, and no scientific logic calls for such a limit; thus (2) is not correct. With (1) and (3) true, (4) is the correct answer.

19. **(1)** Man eats plant foods, such as fruits, vegetables, and grains, which require him to bite (cut) off portions (as with fruits, corn, and others) and to grind vegetables and grains. He eats meat, which requires him to bite (cut) off pieces, tear apart meat fibers, and to crush (grind) the fibers. Hence, man has use for all three kinds of teeth. Thus, (1) is the correct answer. Man, of course, evolved from many animals, but just as a horse's teeth are adapted for grazing and a lion's teeth for eating meat, man's teeth are adapted to his diet of both plant foods and meat, not to what his ancestors ate. Thus, (2) is not correct, nor is (3).

20. **(4)** Paragraph six says that foods high in sugar content promote the growth of certain bacteria which produce acid that causes tooth decay. Thus, (1), (2), and (3) all are true, making (4) the correct answer.

21. **(1)** Paragraph three explains that density is weight per unit of volume. Since 1 milliliter (volume) of water weighs 1 gram (weight), the weight per unit volume is 1 gram per milliliter; therefore, the density of water is 1. If 10 milliliters of mercury weigh 135.5 grams, one milliliter weighs 13.55 grams. And 13.55 grams per milliliter gives a density of 13.55 for mercury. Finally, rounding off the decimal to tenths, we get 13.6, the number of times mercury is denser than water. Thus, (1) is the correct answer.

22. **(3)** Paragraph six states that the total amount of heat in a substance depends on the total molecular energy of the substance. Thus, (3) is the correct answer. The same paragraph states that you need more than a thermometer to measure total amount of heat. Thus, (1) is not a correct choice. The same paragraph also says that the average kinetic energy of the molecules of a substance is the temperature, not the total amount of heat, of the substance. Thus, (2) is not correct.

23. **(1)** The next-to-the-last paragraph states that 1 calorie is the amount of heat required to raise 1 gram of water 1 degree C. The temperature of water in the refrigerator fell 45° C. It lost to the air in the refrigera-

tor as much heat as it would take to raise the temperature of the same amount of water 45° C. The weight of the 100 milliliters of water in the glass at 5° C was almost exactly 100 grams. (It did not weigh exactly 100 grams because a ml of water weighs 1 gram only at 4° C, as stated in paragraph two.) To raise 100 grams of water 1° C takes 100 calories. To raise 100 grams of water 45° takes 45 times as many calories, or 45 × 100 calories, which equals 4500 calories. Thus, (1) is the correct answer.

24. **(3)** The last paragraph states that the Calorie (kilogram-calorie) is a measure of heat-values of foods. Therefore, an amount of food that has 5 Calories provides less heat than an equal amount of food that has 50 Calories. Since heat is a form of energy, the 5-Calorie teaspoonful of sugar substitute provides less heat energy than the 50-Calorie teaspoonful of sugar. Thus, (3) is the correct answer. A healthful food is one that promotes good health. Therefore, it cannot be said, without knowing the needs of the person eating it, that the sugar substitute is or is not more healthful than cane sugar. The smaller amount of energy in the sugar substitute might be more healthful to a fat person and less healthful to a thin person. Thus, (2) is not crorect.

25. **(2)** Paragraph two states that the density of water is less when it is colder or warmer than 4° C than it is when it is at 4° C; therefore, the density of water at 1° C is less than at 4° C. Paragraph four defines specific gravity as a comparison of the density of a substance with the density of water at 4° C. Since the density of water at 1° C is less than the density of water at 4° C, the specific gravity of water at 1° C must be less than the specific gravity of water at 4° C. Thus, (2) is the correct answer.

26. **(4)** Paragraph two states that water weighs less when it is either warmer or colder than 4° C. In any body of water, that part which is at 4° C is densest and sinks to the bottom. As the water becomes colder, it becomes less dense and is pushed upward by the denser water which is at 4° C. The water which becomes cold enough to form ice, at 0° C, is at the upper surface. One result of this fact is that water freezes from the top downward. When natural bodies of water freeze, ice forms on the upper surface. Unless the whole body of water is very shallow, the bottom of the water does not freeze. Therefore, there always is water in which fish can swim instead of being frozen in the ice. The fact that the ice floats shows that it is less dense than the water beneath it, since less dense substances float on more dense substances. Thus, (1), (2), and (3) are true, making (4) the correct answer.

27. **(2)** Paragraph five states that the boiling point of water is 100° C. Paragraph six states that a cupful of boiling water will not melt as much snow as a gallon of water at room temperature. From this we can conclude that the total amount of heat in the gallon of water is greater than the total amount of heat in the cupful. The next-to-the-last paragraph states that total amounts of heat may be expressed in

calories. Therefore, the gallon of water at room temperature contains more calories than the cupful at 100° C. Thus, (2) is the correct answer.

28. **(1)** If the land was bare rock, we can reason that the succession of plants had to be like that of today, beginning with some kind of plant that could live on bare rock and need very little moisture. That plant, then, would be like modern lichens. Thus, (1) is the correct answer. If the succession of plants on the bare rock followed that of today, trees (2), mosses (3), and any other plants, such as ferns (4) would have followed the lichen-like plants. Hence, neither (2), (3), nor (4) is correct.

29. **(3)** Paragraph three notes that the larger "bodies" of mosses form more soil when they die. From this fact we can reason that the still larger bodies of trees (including leaves, branches, and trunks) will form still more soil. Therefore, the rate of soil formation will increase. Thus, (3) is the correct answer.

30. **(2)** A flat, horizontal rock offers a better chance for decaying lichens and bits of windblown dust to accumulate and provide a soil for the growth of mosses. Although lichens can live on steeply inclined—and even vertical—rock faces, common sense tells us that bits of decaying lichens and windblown dust are likely to slide off a rock surface in this position, delaying the accumulation of soil. Thus, (2) is the correct answer. No rounded, slanted rock is mentioned in the question, so (4) cannot be correct.

31. **(1)** After a forest fire, the soil is still available for plant growth, so the plant community does not have to go through the succession beginning with lichens in order to build up a soil. Therefore, a forest community should grow in a much shorter time. Thus, (1) is the correct answer.

32. **(1)** The first answer (1) is a very general answer, but one that must be a reasonable conclusion, for if other plants do not succeed lichens and mosses then the conditions for the growth of the other plants must be lacking. Such conditions actually are lacking in the far antarctic and arctic regions where lichens and mosses can grow, but where it is too cold for seed plants to grow, and continual snows cover any surface on which a soil might accumulate. Thus, (1) is the correct answer. Choices (2) and (3), unlike (1), cannot be deduced logically from the material in the passage, nor does any of this material state anything to support these answers. The fourth answer (4) mentions lichens and mosses growing in soil, but the passage explains that they grow without soil. Thus (4) cannot be correct.

33. **(2)** Paragraph three states that, along with decaying lichens, bits of windblown dust collect in crevices to make the original soil in a rocky environment. Thus, (2) is the correct answer. Nothing in the passage gives any reason to consider darkness as a factor in the succession of plants. Hence, (1) is not correct. Snow is a form of water, which is necessary for the growth of plants, but the question notes this and asks for an agent in addition to water. Hence, (3) is not correct. Since

plants grow in all parts of the world, and some latitudes do not have alternating warm and cold seasons, (4) cannot be a correct choice.

34. **(1)** Paragraph two says that latitude is a measure of distance between the equator and the poles, and that zero degrees latitude is at the equator. Thus, (1) is the correct answer. Paragraph one explains that longitude, not latitude, is measured from the prime meridian which runs through Greenwich, England. Hence, (2) and (3) are incorrect.

35. **(1)** The first paragraph says that degrees of longitude run both east and west to 180°; therefore, 360° is the greatest number of degrees through which a ship could sail.

36. **(4)** Paragraph three says that one degree of latitude is divided into 60 minutes, and the length of one minute is about $1\frac{1}{6}$ miles. Changing $1\frac{1}{6}$ to a proper fraction and multiplying by 60, we get $\frac{7}{6} \times 60 = \frac{420}{60} = 70$. Thus, one degree of latitude equal 70 miles, and (4) is the correct answer.

37. **(2)** In question 36, we worked out how many miles equal one degree of latitude, finding the number to be 70. To find the number of miles equal to a given number of degrees of latitude, we multiply the number of degrees by the number of miles in one degree. Since the North Pole is at 90° north latitude, and New Orleans is at 30° north latitude, the number of degrees between them is 60. Then, $60 \times 70 = 4200$, the number of miles between New Orleans and the North Pole. Thus, (2) is the correct answer.

38. **(1)** Degrees of longitude run east and west from the prime meridian for 180° in each direction. At the equator, the circumference of the earth is divided into 360 equal parts, one for each degree of longitude. Ninety degrees of latitude, running from the equator to a pole, covers ¼ of the earth's circumference. The whole circumference contains $4 \times 90°$, or 360° of latitude. Hence, the circumference of the earth is divided into 360 by (a) the equator, and (b) any meridian of longitude extended all the way around the earth. Therefore, at the equator, one degree of latitude equals one degree of longitude. Thus, (1) is correct. Meridians are all equal in length. Parallels become shorter and shorter as they approach the poles. One degree of latitude represents everywhere approximately 70 miles. One degree of longitude varies from 70 miles at the equator to nothing at the poles. Hence (3) is not correct. The prime meridian runs north and south, and the equator, east and west, so that there is no midpoint between them. Thus, (4) is not correct.

39. **(2)** The first paragraph says that the degrees of longitude run east and west from Greenwich, England, meeting in the Pacific Ocean. Since East St. Louis, Illinois, is west of Greenwich, but not more than 180° west, the longitude must be west longitude. Thus, (2) is the correct answer.

40. **(1)** Since the latitude of either pole is 90° (the highest latitude possible), traveling from a pole, you must go to lower latitudes. Thus, (1) is the correct answer.

41. **(1)** Paragraph one of the passage states that malaria passes from man to the *Anopheles* mosquito to man. Therefore, the mosquito transmits the disease. Thus, (1) is the correct answer. Paragraph two explains that malaria is a blood disease. Because of this fact, it should not be expected that expulsions of matter from the lungs, throat, or nose will spread the disease, and indeed they do not. Hence, (2) is not correct. Since, as paragraph two explains, the life cycle of the malaria parasite takes place in either the bloodstream of man or in the body of a mosquito, foods do not provide an environment in which the parasite can live. Therefore, malaria is not transmitted by food; hence, (3) is not correct.

42. **(2)** Paragraph two explains that if a mosquito bites a malaria sufferer when only the normal forms of the parasite are in the victim's blood, the parasites die in the mosquito's stomach. If this happens, the mosquito cannot transmit the disease. Hence, whether an *Anopheles* mosquito can or cannot transmit malaria depends on the condition of the sufferer's blood when he is bitten. We can only say that whether a mosquito will or will not transmit malaria in any particular instance is uncertain. Thus, (2) is the correct answer, and the other choices must be wrong.

43. **(3)** Paragraph three states that most species of mosquitoes have a substance in their saliva that prevents the clotting of blood. This is of advantage to a mosquito because clotted blood probably would plug up the mosquito's mouthparts. Thus, (3) is the correct answer. Poisoning its victim (1), transmitting malaria (2), and causing the bite to itch (4) are not of any advantage to a mosquito; hence, these choices are all incorrect.

44. **(1)** Paragraph one says that malaria is an alternating host disease, the two hosts being man and mosquito. Man calls the other host (the mosquito, the host that carries the disease from man to man) a vector. From the mosquito's point of view, man carries the disease from mosquito to mosquito, and, therefore, is the vector. Thus, (1) is the correct answer.

45. **(2)** If all the malaria victims in the country were given medicine that would lead to a cure, these people could become reinfected by any mosquitoes that still carried the disease. So, (1) would not be a good first choice. By getting rid of mosquitoes, the people would be putting an end to one of the two alternating hosts in the man-mosquito cycle of malaria. Then, if the medicine was used, the people who were cured would remain cured. Thus, (2) is the correct answer. Building hospitals would not have any direct effect on the alternating host malaria cycle. Hence, (3) is not correct. Choice (4) does not specify what kind of injections would be given and thus is meaningless and incorrect.

46. **(1)** Paragraph two explains the stages which the disease-producing form of the malaria parasites must go through before they arrive at the mosquito's salivary glands from where they may be injected into an animal. It is not reasonable to expect the parasites to go through all the stages in ten seconds, the time given in the question. Therefore, the second man would not become ill with malaria, and (1) is the correct answer.

47. **(2)** Neither the alchemist's belief in base metals, nor his belief that gold is a perfect metal, nor his aim of transmuting one metal into another should cause us to classify him as not being a true scientist. Beliefs and aims are in themselves neither scientific nor unscientific; it is the method by which they are tested that decides whether they rank as scientific or not. Hence, (1), (3), and (4) cannot be correct choices. The last paragraph of the passage states that the alchemist worked with his beliefs and aims as untested assumptions rather than using them as hypotheses to be verified—the scientific manner. For this reason, the alchemist was unscientific. Thus, (2) is the correct answer.

48. **(3)** The first paragraph of the passage states directly that the Egyptians were not interested in chemical theories and that they made chemical discoveries by trial and error; thus, (1) is incorrect and (3) is the correct answer. Nothing in the passage states or implies that Egyptians made any use of the idea of the unity of nature; hence, (2) is wrong. With (1) and (2) incorrect, (4) must be wrong.

49. **(3)** The activities of the alchemists, as described in the passage, were clearly far from abstract theory; thus, (1) cannot be a correct choice. The passage says that the Greeks were not interested in experimenting in science; hence, (2) is not correct. The interest of the Greeks in abstract theory is stated in detail in the passage; thus (3) is the correct answer. Choice (4) is incorrect, since gold is mined and its discovery was not a matter of chemistry at all.

50. **(4)** In the part of the passage concerning the Greeks, there is no material that would warrant the conclusions that a substance exposed to fire would absorb other elements or that the fire would absorb some elementary properties of the substance. Therefore, (1) and (3) are incorrect. The idea of oxidation is a modern one and could not have been known to the Greeks. Thus, (2) is incorrect. That the ancient Greeks believed a substance is broken down into its constituent elements when it burns is stated directly in the third paragraph, making (4) the correct answer.

51. **(3)** The last sentence of the last paragraph states that alchemy "paved the way for the development of chemistry," thus making (3) the correct answer. The fact that a science of chemistry supplanted alchemy means that alchemy no longer fluorished; hence, (2) is not correct.

52. **(4)** The last paragraph states that "the work of the alchemist was not in vain" and that this work led to the accumulation of much factual knowledge and the devising of new chemical apparatus. The same paragraph says that alchemy taught the chemist to beware of false

hypotheses. Thus (1) is false and (2) and (3) are true, making (4) the correct answer.

53. **(4)** The first paragraph states that the Egyptian chemists were not interested in chemical theories, while the second paragraph says that the Greeks were interested only in the theoretical aspects of chemistry. Thus, (1) and (2) are wrong. The third paragraph details how the Greeks, not the Egyptians, divided substances into four "elements." Hence, (3) is wrong.

54. **(3)** There are four processes that repeat themselves over and over in the nitrogen cycle. These may be seen by following the arrows in the diagram. The cycles are (1) atmospheric nitrogen, plant protein, organic matter in soil, nitrates, atmospheric nitrogen; (2) atmospheric nitrogen, plant protein, animal protein, organic matter in soil, nitrates, nitrogen in atmosphere; (3) nitrates, plant protein, organic matter in soil, nitrates; and (4) nitrates, plant protein, animal protein, organic matter in soil, nitrates. Thus, (3) is the correct answer.

55. **(1)** Paragraph three explains how nitrogen-fixing bacteria which live in the roots of legumes—one of which is clover—take nitrogen out of the air and make it available to plants. Thus, (1) is the correct answer. Soil is not an animal that can become tired; it can become "exhausted," which means that it has lost one or more constituents necessary for plant growth. Such soil will not become fertile again simply by "resting." Hence, (2) is not correct. Denitrifying bacteria remove nitrogen from, rather than put it into, soil, as explained in the next-to-the-last paragraph. Hence, (3) is not correct.

56. **(2)** The last paragraph describes how lightning is responsible for a minor amount of nitrogen in soil. If nitrogen-fixing bacteria were to disappear, some atmospheric nitrogen would be converted by lightning into nitrogen compounds that can be used by plants. Thus, (2) is the correct answer. The only plants that can fix atmospheric nitrogen are legumes and they do so only because of the nitrogen-fixing bacteria that live on their roots. Thus, (1) and (3) are not correct. Denitrifying bacteria break down certain nitrates in the soil as part of a process that puts nitrogen into the atmosphere; but without nitrogen-fixing bacteria, there eventually would be no more nitrates in the soil on which denitrifying bacteria could work. Thus, (4) is not correct.

57. **(2)** The nitrogen cycle shows that animal protein (meat) comes only from plant protein. Even those animals that eat only meat eat animals that eat plant proteins. So, plants had to exist on land before animals could. Thus, (2) is the correct answer and (1) is incorrect. Crawling fish (4) and amphibians (3) were among the first land animals, but, being animals, they were dependent on plants for proteins. Thus, (3) and (4) are not correct.

58. **(4)** The last paragraph explains how lightning forms nitrogen compounds which find their way into the soil. Thus, the first plants to try living on land found usable nitrogen in the sandy soil. Hence, (1) is true.

The question says that there were plants in the earth's waters before plants grew on land. Masses of dead water plants washed ashore and decomposed by bacteria could have provided nitrogen for the first land plants, just as, according to the nitrogen cycle, decomposed plants provide nitrogen to the organic matter in the soil. Thus, (3) is true. With (1) and (3) true, (4) is the correct answer.

59. (2) Paragraph one states that nitrogen is the most important element in proteins and proteins are the basic constituents of protoplasm. Thus, (2) is the correct answer. Nitrogen makes up four-fifths of the air that animals breathe or take into their bodies by means of gills or other organs as animals satisfy their need for oxygen. The nitrogen is breathed out or is expelled in some other manner entirely unused and unchanged. Hence, for animals, nitrogen is not a necessary part of air. Thus, (1) is not correct. Nitrogen, being so important a constituent of protoplasm, must reasonably be an important constituent of foods; but neither nitrogen nor any other element that goes into making foodstuffs can be said to be a food itself. Thus, (3) is not correct.

60. (4) Answers (1) and (2) may be obtained from paragraph three. If (1) is true, then the ring from which the moon formed must have been farther from the earth than Saturn's rings are from that planet. From this fact and the lesser weight of the earth, we can reason that the earth's tidal force on its dust ring was less than Saturn's tidal force on its rings. Hence, (3) is true. With (1), (2) and (3) being true, (4) is the correct answer.

61. (2) The first paragraph of the passage states that Saturn's third, or "gray," ring is conspicuous only when it passes over the sunlit disk of Saturn. Thus, (2) is the correct answer. The fact that (2) is the correct answer logically makes (1) incorrect. Since the third ring is the inner ring, it would be obscured by the two outer rings when Saturn's rings are seen edge-on. Thus, (3) is not correct.

62. (4) The last two sentences of paragraph three explain that Saturn's enormous tidal force would break up any satellite as close to the planet as the rings are. Thus, (4) is the correct answer. The last paragraph states that the rings are made up of ice crystals or snow and are quite thin. A fully formed satellite colliding with the rings would not be damaged by them. Thus, (1) is not correct. According to the passage, no satellite could form at a distance as near to Saturn as its rings are; hence, no satellite formed that could have fallen upon the planet. Thus, (2) is not correct. The first part of (3) assumes that at one time satellites formed close to Saturn, but this is incorrect for the same reason that (2) is incorrect.

63. (3) The passage explains that all the planets once were probably surrounded by rings of matter. Thus, (3) is the correct answer. The passage states that Saturn's rings are "testimony of the old days of creation"; hence, the rings are not a recent development, and (1) is incorrect. Nothing is said in the passage about dust rings being formed around Saturn from volcanoes on that planet. Thus, (2) is not correct.

64. (3) The third paragraph mentions Saturn's ten known satellites. Thus, (3) is the correct answer, and (1) must be incorrect. The same paragraph says that Saturn is 7600 times more massive than the earth's moon. Hence, (2) is incorrect. Paragraph three also says that Saturn is 95 times heavier than the earth, not that Saturn has a satellite 95 times as heavy as the earth. Hence, (4) is not correct.

65. (4) The second paragraph says that Saturn is the only planet surrounded by rings; hence, (1) cannot be correct. Paragraph four says that Saturn's rings are probably made up of ice crystals; hence, (2) is not correct. Paragraph four also says that the rings of Saturn cannot be more than 1000 feet thick; hence, (3) is incorrect. Since, (1), (2), and (3) are all incorrect, (4) is the correct answer.

GLOSSARY: TERMS YOU SHOULD KNOW

Users of this book will find this glossary an indispensable tool for coordinating the material of the several science passages. This listing is meant to provide a basis for comprehension of the language used in those passages.

The terms are keyed so that the reader can refer to them in the text passages. The letter and number following a word refer to the subject area and the passage in which the term may be found.

Dg—The Diagnostic Test   C—Physics
A—Biology   D—Earth Science
B—Chemistry   S—The Simulated Test

EXAMPLES: Dg-IV refers to the fourth passage in The Diagnostic Test.
           B-4 refers to the fourth passage in the chemistry section.
           S-II refers to the second passage in The Simulated Test.

Terms keyed by letter and number are defined fully in the **Scientific terms defined** section which follows the passage indicated. Terms not keyed to a passage are important basic scientific terms, and, as they may be encountered on the GED Test, are fully defined in this glossary. Terms within a definition in this glossary followed by *(qv)* are defined elsewhere in the glossary.

absolute   The Kelvin temperature scale. *See* **Kelvin.** (Dg–I)
acceleration   C–3
alchemist   One who practiced alchemy, which was the empirical and speculative forerunner of chemistry, and which flourished during the Middle Ages.
alloy   C–2
amplitude   In wave motion, the distance of the crest or the trough of a wave from the midline; the greatest displacement of the medium from the rest position.
anisotopic   B–2
anode   A positive electrode, as in an electric cell.
antheridium   A–4
antibody   A chemical substance with which the body opposes the toxins of harmful bacteria.
apogee   The point in the orbit of a celestial body that is farthest from the center of the orbit; as the apogee of an artificial earth satellite, the point farthest from the center of the earth.
archegonium   A–4
atom   The smallest particle of a chemical element that takes part in a chemical change. (Dg–II)

atomic weight   Relative weight of an atom when compared to the weight of a carbon atom, which is taken as 12.00.

atomic weight unit (awu)   B–2

axial rotation   Rotation of a body around its axis. (Dg–III)

bacteria   Any of a class of microscopic plants having rodlike, spiral, round, or filamentous bodies; important to man as decomposers (*qv*), as aids to digestion, and as producers of disease through chemical effects.

barb   A–1

barbule   A–1

barometer   The most common instrument used to measure the pressure of the earth's atmosphere.

bedrock   The surface of the earth's crust directly beneath the covering of soil, sand, and loose rock.

biosphere   A–2

bond, chemical   *See* **chemical bond.**

Boyle's Law   A physico-chemical law defining the changes in volume of a gas which accompany changes in pressure. (S–II)

calcareous   Composed of, containing, or like calcium carbonate or limestone.

calorie   C–5

canine   Of or relating to dogs; specifically, one of the two upper and two lower fang-shaped teeth in man and certain other mammals.

carbon dioxide   A gaseous chemical compound resulting from the complete burning of carbon in air or pure oxygen.

carbon monoxide   A gaseous chemical compound resulting from the incomplete burning of carbon.

carnivorous   Meat-eating.

catalyst   A substance that initiates and carries on a chemical reaction, but does not itself enter into the products of that reaction.

cathode   The negative electrode, as in an electric cell.

cell membrane   The membrane that surrounds the protoplasm of a cell. (S–I)

Celsius   The temperature scale in which 0° is the freezing point of water and 100° is the boiling point of water; named after its inventor, Anders Celsius, of Sweden; also known as the centigrade scale. (S–IV)

centigrade   *See* **Celsius.** (S–IV)

chemical bond   A force that attracts atoms to one another and binds them together, and which is broken and remade when atoms recombine through chemical reaction.

chemical reaction   The interaction of two or more substances, resulting in chemical changes in them; that is, the substances undergo a change in chemical composition, due to an increase, decrease, or rearrangement of the atoms that make up the substance.

chemosynthesizer   A–3

chromatin   The part of a cell nucleus that stains deeply with basic dyes. (S–I)

chromosome   Threadlike structures within almost all plant and animal cells; containers of the hereditary mechanism of cells. (S–I)

circulatory system   The system of tubular vessels that carries blood and lymph in animals.

compound   A–3, B–1

concentric   Having a common center, as of circles, spheres, and other closed geometric figures.

conduction   Transfer of heat from molecule to molecule through the mechanism of molecular collision; also, the transfer of electricity through certain substances, mainly metals; also, the transfer of sound through materials.

conductometer   C–5

conductor   A substance or material that transfers heat, electricity, or sound.

conservation of energy, law of   The physical law that states that energy may be transformed but not created or destroyed.

conservation of mass (matter), law of   The physical law which states that mass may be changed in form but not created or destroyed.

consumer   A–5

contour feather   A–1

convection   C–5

core   D–5

crust   D–5

cyclotron   A device that accelerates heavy atomic particles, such as protons; an "atom smasher."

cytoplasm   All the protoplasm of a cell outside the nucleus.

DDT   Dichlorodiphenyltrichloroethane, a colorless, odorless, crystalline insecticide.

debris   D–4

decomposer   A bacterium, fungus, or mold that breaks down dead plants and animals into simple substances that can be used for the nutrition of plants. (S–V)

denitrifying bacteria   Soil bacteria which break down certain nitrates into simpler substances, including nitrous oxide which escapes into the atmosphere. (S–IX)

density   C–4

dentine   Bonelike material of a tooth located directly beneath the enamel. (S-III)

deoxyribonucleic acid   The molecular constituent of chromosomes which contains the genes. (S–I)

dermal covering   A–1

deuterium   An isotope of hydrogen having one electron and a nucleus, known as a deuteron, which contains one proton and one neutron.

deuteron   *See* **deuterium.**

diffraction   A–1

DNA   *See* **deoxyribonucleic acid.**

down   A–1

ecological   A–3

ecosystem   A–3

ectoplasm   The protoplasm near a cell's surface. (S–I)

electrochemical   B–3

electromotive   B–3

electron   The smallest possible particle of negative electricity; the constituent of electric current.

electron microscope   A microscope that uses a beam of electrons to form images of the objects being examined.

element   B–1

elliptical   In the shape of an ellipse: a closed, plane, oval curve. (Dg–III)

embryo   The early stages in the development of plants and animals which reproduce sexually; the organism before it has assumed its characteristic form.

enamel   The hard, white covering of teeth. (S–III)

energy   The capacity to perform work.

enzyme   An organic catalyst which promotes chemical reactions in living organisms.

erosion   D–4

evaporation   D–4

excrete   To separate and eliminate or discharge undesirable substances from blood, tissues, or protoplasm.

Fahrenheit   The temperature scale in which the freezing point of water is 32° and the boiling point of water is 212°; named for its inventor, the German scientist, Gabriel Daniel Fahrenheit.

fault   D–1

filoplume   A–1

flagellated   Having one or more flagella, long hairlike or whiplike extensions of protoplasm by means of which certain one-celled organisms and certain cells swim about. (S–VII)

flood plain   A plain cut by the erosion of a river and then built up by sediment from the river's water in time of flood.

fluorescence   The property of certain substances which enables them to radiate light when stimulated by radiation of a different wavelength.

fluoridation   The addition of fluorides to water and dentrifices for the purpose of retarding tooth decay. (S–III)

follicle   A–1

force   Energy or strength brought to bear or exerted so as to produce, destroy, or change motion.

fossil   Any remains, impression, or trace of an animal or plant of past geological ages that has been preserved in the earth's crust.

frequency   The number of waves passing a given point in a unit of time, usually one second.

friction   D–3

fungi   A–2

gametophyte   A–4

genetic code   The manner in which hereditary traits are transmitted from parent to offspring by means of DNA (qv) and RNA (qv). (S–I)

geocentric   With the earth as a center; an ancient and discredited idea of the structure of the universe. (Dg–III)

geology   The science that deals with the history, structure, and composition of the earth and its life, especially as recorded in rocks.

germinate   A–4

glacial period One of several periods in the history of the earth when glaciers covered a major part of the earth's surface. (Dg–IV)

glacier A large body of ice that moves slowly down a slope or valley or spreads outward on any land surface; specifically, the ice that covered much of the earth during glacial periods. (Dg–IV)

gram A unit of mass and weight in the metric system and equal to 1/1000 of a kilogram, or approximately the weight of one cubic centimeter of water at its greatest density. (S–IV)

gravitation The force of attraction between all bodies in the universe.

groundwater D–4

habitat A–3

heavy water Water in which the deuterium (*qv*) substitutes for the normal form of hydrogen; D_2O.

heliocentric With the sun as a center; the astronomical theory that considers the sun as the center of the solar system. (Dg–III)

herbivorous Plant-eating.

heterogenous B–1

homogenous B–1

host A plant or animal inside which or upon which a parasite lives and feeds. (S–VII)

hydrate To take up or combine with water; a compound or complex ion formed by the combination of water and some other substance.

hydrologic cycle D–4

hydrosphere D–2

hypothesis B–2

incisor In man and other mammals, a cutting tooth located in the front of the mouth. (S–III)

inertia D–3

infiltration D–4

infrared Radiation with wavelengths not much below (longer than) the wavelengths of visible red light.

inorganic A–3

insolation Solar radiation received by the earth or other planets.

insulator C–5

interglacial period In the history of the earth, one of the periods that were between glacial periods. (Dg–IV)

ion B–2

isotope A–2

Kelvin The temperature scale in which the zero point (absolute zero) is 273 degrees below Celsius, or centigrade, zero, and a degree has the same range as a Celsius degree; the absolute temperature scale; named for its inventor, the British mathematician and physicist, William Thompson, first Lord Kelvin. (Dg–I)

kilogram The basic metric unit of mass and weight, nearly equal to 1000 cubic centimeters of water at maximum density. (S–IV)

kilogram-calorie *See* **calorie.** (S–IV)

landslip   D–1

latitude   Distance north or south of the earth's equator measured through 90 degrees, each of which locates an imaginary circle, called a parallel of latitude, and which has the earth's axis as a center. (S–VI)

lava   D–3

lichen   Any of a group of plants made up of an alga and a fungus living in a relationship of mutual benefit upon a hard surface, such as a rock. (S–V)

lipid   Any of various substances including fats, waxes, and phosphotides, some of which make up the principle structural components of living cells. (S–I)

lithosphere   D–1

lodestone   C–2

longitude   Distance measured through 180 degrees east and west of a semicircle reaching from pole to pole, passing through Greenwich, England, and called the prime meridian; other meridians pass through each of the total of 360 degrees of longitude. (S–VI)

longitudinal wave   A wave in which the motion of the particles is in the same direction as that in which the wave is advancing, as a sound wave.

magma   D–1

magnetic pole   C–2

magnetism   C–2

malaria   A disease caused by a mosquito-borne parasite and characterized by regularly alternating chills and fever. (S–VII)

mantle   D–5

mantle rock   D–5

mass   C–4

mass spectrograph   B–2

meridian   A semicircle of longitude (*qv*). (S–VI)

metabolism   A–2

metric system   C–4, S–IV

milliliter   A measure of volume equal to one one-thousandth of a liter. (S–IV)

millimeter   A measure of length equal to one one-thousandth of a meter; abbreviated "mm." (Dg–I)

mixture   B–1

molar   A crushing and grinding tooth of man and mammals. (S–III)

molecule   Dg–I, B–4

molt   A–1

mono-nuclidic   B–2

multiple proportions, law of   When the same elements combine to form different compounds, they do so in the ratio of small whole numbers.

mutant   An organism differing from its parents in one or more characteristics that can be inherited.

nebula   In astronomy, any mass ·of cloudlike appearance and vast extent in space, and composed of gases and/or dust particles.

nematode   A–2

neutron   B–2

nitrate   Any of several compounds of nitrogen and oxygen in certain specific proportions. (S–IX)

nitrifying bacteria   Bacteria that live in soil and change organic matter in the soil to nitrates. (S–IX)

nitrogen cycle   The endless process in which nitrogen in the air becomes part of plants and animals, then certain nitrogen compounds, and then returns to the atmosphere. (S–IX)

nitrogen-fixing bacteria   Bacteria that live on the roots of plants called legumes and which convert atmospheric nitrogen to nitrogen compounds that plants can use in their nutrition. (S–IX)

nucleolus   A small body inside the nucleus (*qv*) of a cell; carrier of RNA (*qv*) and the genetic code in the process of cell division.

nucleoplasm   The protoplasmic substance of which the nucleus of a cell is made. (S–I)

nucleus   A rounded and usually central mass of denser protoplasm in a cell; container of DNA, RNA, and genes, and therefore, transmitter of hereditary characteristics; control center for the cell's activities. (S–I)

orbit   The path described by one object revolving around another, as a planet revolving around the sun. (Dg–III)

organic   A–3

organism   Any live plant or animal. (Dg–V)

outcrop   D–5

oxidation   A chemical process involving the loss of electrons by an atom or group of atoms; also the combination of oxygen with another substance.

paleontology   The study of the life of the far past through the examination of fossil and geological evidence.

parallel   In geography, a circle of latitude (*qv*). (S–VI)

parasite   A plant or animal that lives upon or within another organism (the host), and feeds upon or otherwise injures the host (*qv*). (S–VII)

particulate   Made up of minute separate particles. (Dg–V)

perigee   The point in the orbit of a celestial body that is closest to the center of the orbit; as the perigee of an artificial earth satellite, the point closest to the center of the earth.

periodic table   An arrangement of chemical elements based on the fact that when the elements are arranged in order of their atomic numbers the elements show a periodic variation in most of their properties.

pesticide   A–2

photoelectric   The property of certain substances of emitting electrons when in the path of light or other types of radiation.

photon   A quantum or parcel of radiant energy, such as a photon of light.

photosynthesis   The process by which green plants produce starch from carbon dioxide and water, using the energy of sunlight.

photosynthesizer   A–3

plasma membrane   The cell membrane (*qv*). (S–I)

polymer   A chemical compound consisting of large (usually) chainlike molecules formed by the combining of smaller molecules called monomers.

potential   B–3

power   In physics, the rate of doing work.

precipitation   D–4

producer A–5

proton B–2

protoplasm The living substance of which all cells of plants and animals are made; living matter. (S–I)

quill A–1

radiation The emission of any rays, wave motion, or particles (e.g., beta particles, neutrons) from any source.

radioactive A–2

reaction B–4

reduction B–3

replication A process in which a molecule produces a new molecule like the original; loosely, the reproduction of daughter cells identical to the parent cells. (Dg–V)

ribonucleic acid In the cell nucleus, a compound that picks up genetic information from deoxyribonucleic acid (DNA) (*qv*) and transmits it to the entire cell. (S–I)

RNA *See* **ribonucleic acid.** (S–I)

runoff D–4

salivary glands Animal glands that produce saliva. (S–VII)

salt B–5

satellite D–3

secrete By an organism, to form and give off certain substances, such as saliva.

seismology The study of earthquakes and other earth vibrations.

shaft A–1

solar system The sun, the planets and their satellites, the asteroids that revolve around the sun, and certain swarms of meteors. (Dg–III)

solubility B–5

solution B–1

sound wave A longitudinal wave (*qv*) in any material medium regardless of whether it can be heard or not.

spore A–4

sporophyte A–4

standard pressure Atmospheric pressure equal to the weight of a column of mercury 760 millimeters high. (Dg–I)

stratosphere The layer of the earth's atmosphere directly above the troposphere (*qv*) and in which the temperature remains fairly constant.

strontium-90 A–2

sublimation The process in which, following a rise in temperature, a solid changes directly to a gas, bypassing the liquid state. (Dg–II)

submicroscopic Too small to be seen with a microscope using light.

tectonic earthquake D–1

thermal conductivity C–5

transpiration The process by which plants give off water, in the form of vapor, to the atmosphere. (D–4)

transverse wave A wave in which the motion of the particles is at right angles to the direction in which the wave is moving, as in light, radio, and radar waves.

trimethylamine A chemical compound which is a gas twice as heavy as air. (Dg–I)

tritium A radioactive isotope of hydrogen having an atomic weight three times that of ordinary hydrogen.

troposphere The lowest layer of the earth's atmosphere, from 7 to 10 miles deep depending on the latitude and the season of the year, and the site of all weather changes.

tsunami D–1

ultramicroscope A microscope that uses scattered light to make visible particles too small to be seen with an ordinary microscope.

ultraviolet Radiation with wavelengths above (shorter than) those of visible violet light.

vacuole Within the cytoplasm (*qv*) of a cell, spherical spaces that contain air, water, or chemical substances.

Van de Graaff generator B–2

vane A–1

vapor The gaseous state of matter as distinguished from the solid and liquid states. (Dg–I)

vector In biology, an organism, such as a mosquito, that transmits a disease-producing factor, such as a malaria parasite (*qv*). (S–VII)

velocity C–3

virus A submicroscopic infective body that may exist either as a living organism in a host (*qv*) or as a nonliving molecule. (Dg–V)

volcanic earthquake D–1

volcanism The conditions and phenomena connected with volcanoes and volcanic action.

water vapor D–2

wavelength In wave motion, the distance between any two similar parts of adjoining waves, as the distance from the crest of one wave to the crest of the following wave.

wave motion The regular vibration of particles in a medium in the form of longitudinal waves (*qv*) or transverse waves (*qv*).

weight The force with which a body is attracted toward the earth or other astronomical body by gravitation.

work That which is accomplished by a force moving through a distance; measured in foot-pounds, kilogram-meters, gram-centimeters, etc.

zenith In astronomy, the position in the sky directly overhead.

zygote A–4